W9-BUT-001

ELEMENTARY PHYSICS

NOTES

COLES EDITORIAL BOARD

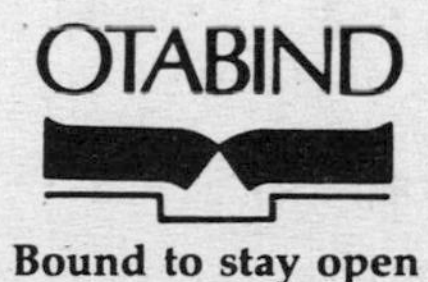

Publisher's Note

Otabind (Ota-bind). This book has been bound using the patented Otabind process. You can open this book at any page, gently run your finger down the spine, and the pages will lie flat.

ISBN 0-7740-3413-0

COLES PUBLISHING COMPANY
TORONTO—CANADA
PRINTED IN CANADA

Manufactured by Webcom Limited
Cover finish: Webcom's Exclusive **Duracoat**

CONTENTS

Unit 1

MECHANICS

MEASUREMENTS

The English and Metric tables of length, mass, volume and liquid measure as studied in earlier grades should be reviewed.

Two systems of measurement exist, the English system, sometimes called the F.P.S. (foot-pound-second) system, and the Metric system, otherwise known as the C.G.S. (centimetre-gram-second) system. The former is used for ordinary every day measurements, while the latter is generally used for scientific measurement.

The standards in the two systems are:–

	Length	Mass	Time
English (F.P.S.) System	yard	pound	second
Metric (C.G.S.) System	metre	kilogram	second

For ordinary measurements these units are not always convenient. Hence the more commonly used units are:–

	Length	Mass	Time
English System	foot	pound	second
Metric System	centimetre	gram	second

The connecting links between the two systems are given in the following table:–

English	Metric	Metric	English
1 yard	0.9144 metre	1 metre	39.37 inches
1 inch	2.54 c.m.	1 kilometre	0.6214 mile
1 mile	1.609 k.m.	1 litre	1.76 pints
1 pound	453.6 gram	1 kilogram	2.205 pounds

Certain *derived units* should also be known.

(a) 1 Imperial gallon of pure water at 62°F weighs 10 pounds and has a volume of 277.27 cubic inches.

(b) 1 litre contains 1000 cc.

APPROXIMATE NUMBERS

Exact numbers arise only from counting. The number of eggs in a dozen or students enrolled at a school are exact numbers. However, all measurements made with instruments are approximate numbers.

The *precision* of a measurement depends on the size of the smallest unit used. Tool making might warrant measurements "to the nearest 1/10,000 inch" while measurements to the nearest 1/8 inch are usually adequate for woodworking.

The length of the line A B can be measured to the nearest ½ inch

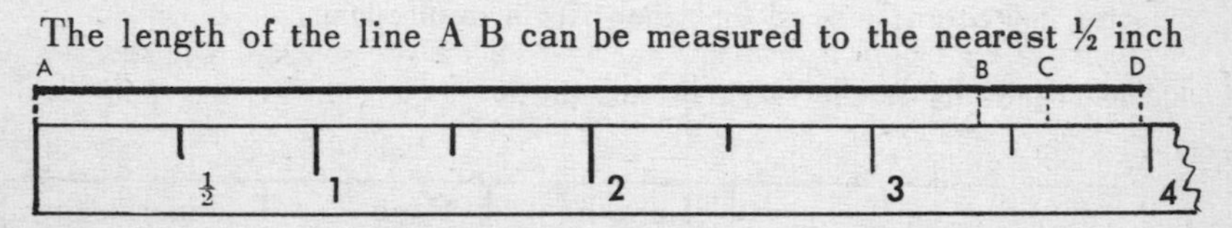

with the ruler shown. It would be recorded as 3½ inches. The precision of the measurement should always be indicated in the recording, for example, A D would be recorded not as simply 4 inches, but as $4\frac{0}{2}$ inches, to show that the smallest unit used is ½ inch.

Recorded measurements such as 15.1 cm, 15.0 cm and 15.3 cm tell us that the smallest unit used was 1/10 cm or 1 mm. Similarly 2.001 inches or 0.003 inches indicate that the measurements are precise to the nearest 1/1000 inch.

Significant Digits of an approximate number are those which tell us the total number of smallest units in the measurement. The following table gives some examples:

Item	Measurement	Smallest unit of Measure	Number of Smallest units	Number of Significant Digits
1	134 in.	1 in.	134	3
2	2.96 cm	.01 cm	296	3
3	2.960 cm	.001 cm	2960	4
4	0.00209 kgm	.00001 kg	209	3
5	1300 in.	1 in.	1300	4
6	1300 in. (to nearest 100 in.)	100 in.	13	2
7	13x10^2 in.	100	13	2
8	7 2/5 lb.	1/5 lb.	37 (37/5)	2
9	8 ft. 5 in.	1 in.	101	3
10	4 lb. 2 oz.	1 oz.	66	2

Points to remember about significant digits:

1. The final zeros in a decimal number are always significant as in item 3 of the table.

2. Zeros on the left of a decimal number whether inside or outside the decimal point as in item 4, are not significant digits.

3. Whether or not the final zeros of a whole number are significant should be stated with the measurement as in item 6, or it may be indicated by powers of 10 as in item 7.

4. The digits in the numerator of a fraction are always significant. Mixed numbers are changed to improper fractions for this purpose.

The *Accuracy* of a measurement is determined by the number of significant digits. For example, the length of the line A D in the previous example, to the nearest ½ inch, would be recorded as $4\frac{0}{2}$ inches, as would any line coming between $3\frac{3}{4}$ and $4\frac{1}{4}$ inches. In other words, when measuring to the nearest ½ inch, the maximum possible error would be ¼ inch, which is $6\frac{1}{4}$% (¼/4 x 100) of the length of the line. But, in measuring a line 400 inches long with the same precision, the possible error would be only 1/16 of 1%, (¼/400 x 100).

Calculations with Approximate Numbers

The results of calculations should show no greater accuracy than that of the least accurate of the measurements used. Since accuracy is determined by the number of significant digits, then the answers to calculations with approximate numbers should be rounded off to the same number of significant digits as contained in the least accurate measurement.

Examples:

1. Add 1.234
   1.2
   0.341

   Total 2.775

   Proper answer 2.8

2. Subtract 3.234
   1.2

   Difference 2.034

   Proper answer 2.0

3. Divide 1.4412 by 1.2
   Quotient = 0.1201

   Proper answer 0.12

4. Multiply 2.345 by 4
   Product = 9.380

   Proper answer 9

MOTION and FORCE

MOTION

All motion is relative. One point is said to be in motion relative to another point when the straight line joining the two points changes in either direction or length. If we stand in one spot we are motionless with respect to the earth but since the earth revolves about its axis and about the sun, our motion relative to the sun would trace a rather complex path. Things which do not move with respect to the earth will be considered to be at rest.

Speed is the word used to express rate of motion and its units are miles per hr., ft. per sec., m. p. sec. etc.

Velocity is defined as the rate of change of position and it involves the *direction* of the change as well as the speed at which the change takes place. A body travels at *uniform velocity* when it covers equal distances in equal periods of time.

VECTOR QUANTITIES

Since velocity involves direction as well as speed it may be represented by a directed line segment (an arrow) whose length is drawn to a convenient scale representing magnitude, eg., 1 cm could be used to represent 10 miles p.hr. Thus velocity is defined as a vector quantity.

SCALAR QUANTITIES

Quantities chosen to represent magnitude only and that do not involve a direction are called scalar quantities. Examples are speed, mass, volume and temperature.

VECTOR DIAGRAMS

Suppose you are travelling in a boat at 10 mi. p.h. downstream in a river that flows at 4 mi. p.h. The velocity, (direction and speed) of the boat can be represented by a vector A B, fig. (i), using a scale of say, 1 cm = 2 mi. p.h. The river's velocity may be represented by vector B C drawn to the same scale. If the vectors are added to each other as shown, then the net or resultant velocity of the boat (direction and magnitude) is given by the length and direction of vector A C when the same scale is applied.

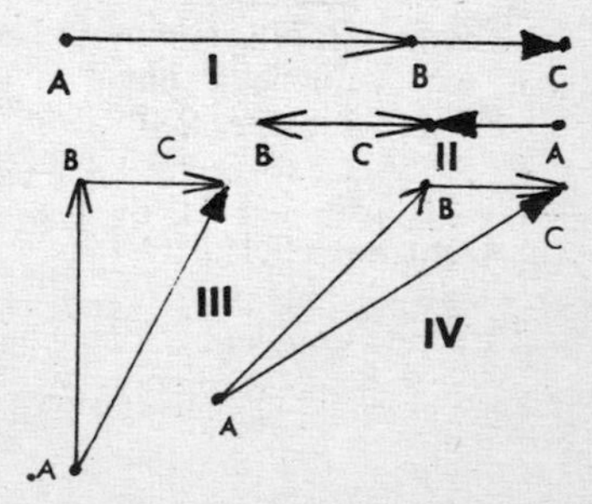

Similarly, in travelling against the stream, the net speed and direction of the boat is given by the vector A C (to scale) in fig. (ii). In figure (iii) the same velocities of boat and river are depicted to the same scale but this time the boat is travelling perpendicularly (A B) to the current (B C). Fig. (iv) represents the case of driving the boat at some angle (<ABC) to the current. In each case the vector A C gives the direction, and its length to scale, gives the resultant speed, of the boat.

ACCELERATION

Suppose a car is put in motion so that in the first second it travels 10 feet in the second second it travels 20 feet and in the third second it travels 30 feet. Its velocity during the first second is 10 f.p.s., during the second is 20 f.p.s. and the third, 30 f.p.s. In each second the velocity increased by 10 f.p.s. In other words it accelerated at the rate of 10 f.p.s. every second. We say its acceleration is 10 ft. per sec., per sec. or 10 ft. per sec^2. From this simple illustration of acceleration a general set of formulae relating velocity, time, distance and acceleration can be developed.

Let u be the initial velocity, a the acceleration and v the final velocity, then:

Initial velocity = u ft. per sec. or cm/sec. etc.
Velocity at end of 2nd second = $u + a$
" " " " 3rd second = $u + 2a$
" " " " t seconds = $v = u + ta$

$v = u + at$ ------ Equation 1.

If an object is accelerated from rest then u = o, and

$v = at$ ---------------- 2.

The average velocity when acceleration is uniform is ½ the sum of the initial and final velocities

$$\therefore \text{Average velocity} = \frac{u + v}{2}$$

Now let the distance in t seconds be s, then distance = ave. velocity x time.

$$\therefore s = \frac{(u + v)}{2} t \text{ ---------------------------- 3.}$$

Substituting for v from 1, $s = \frac{(2u + at)}{2} t$

$$\therefore s = ut + \tfrac{1}{2}at^2 \text{ ---------------------- 4.}$$

It is left to the student to develop the equation,–

$$v^2 = u^2 + 2as \quad \text{-------------------------} \quad 5.$$

Examples

1. A car starts from rest and reaches 60 mph in 4 seconds, what is its acceleration?

   Solution: $u = 0$
   $v = 60 \text{ mph} = 88 \text{ f.p.s.}$
   $t = 4 \text{ seconds}$
   using equation 2, $v = at$,
   $$a = \frac{v}{t} = \frac{88}{4} = 22 \text{ ft. per sec.}^2$$

2. At what rate must a rocket accelerate from lift-off in order to attain a velocity of 25000 f.p.s. at an altitude of 100 miles.

   Solution: $u = 0$
   $s = 100 \text{ miles} = 528{,}000 \text{ feet}$
   $v = 25000 \text{ f.p.s.}$
   $a = ?$
   using equation 5
   $$v^2 = u^2 + 2as$$
   $$(25000)^2 = 0 + 2 \times a \times 528{,}000$$
   $$a = \frac{25000 \times 25000}{2 \times 528{,}000} = 592 \text{ f.p.s.}^2$$

NEWTON'S FIRST LAW of MOTION and INERTIA

"A body will remain in a state of rest or of uniform motion in a straight line unless compelled by some external force to change that state". In other words the velocity (a vector quantity) of a body will remain unchanged unless acted upon by an external force (another vector quantity).

The tendency of the body mentioned in Newton's first law to remain at rest or in a state of uniform motion is a result of the *inertia* of the body and the greater the *mass* of a body the greater is its inertia. The trick of pulling a table cloth from beneath a setting of fine chinaware without making a mess on the floor is possible only because of the inertia of the china.

It takes many tugs to move an ocean liner because of its great mass or inertia and for the same reason the liner would easily crush a small craft against a dock while coasting slowly in that direction.

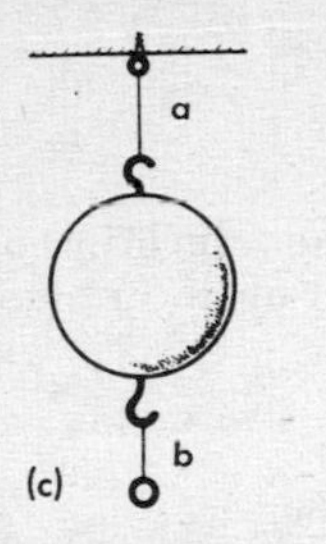

If the lower thread is pulled slowly the upper thread will break first because it supports the kgm weight as well as the force of the pull. If pulled with a jerk the lower thread would break because of the inertia of the weight.

NEWTON'S SECOND LAW, ACCELERATION and FORCE

The "pick-up" or "get-away" of a car depends on the power of its engine; in other words, the greater the force available the greater will be the acceleration. Also, a car of greater mass (inertia) will require a greater force to attain the same acceleration.

Thus Newtons second law: the acceleration of a body is proportional to the applied force, is inversely proportional to the mass of the body and is in the direction of the applied force.

Mathematically the law may be expressed as,–

$$\text{Force} = \text{Mass} \times \text{Acceleration}$$

or

$$F = Ma$$

In the MKS system, M is measured in kg
a is in meters per sec.^{2}

$\therefore F = Ma = \text{kg meters per sec.}^2$

For abreviation one kg-m per sec^2 is called one *NEWTON*
or $1N = 1$ kg-m per sec^2

The newton is an *absolute unit of force,* it depends only on the definitions of the standard units of mass, length and time, i.e. the kg, meter and second.

Gravitational Units of Force depend on the force of gravity. For example a force of one pound is the gravitational force that the earth exerts on a mass of one pound and it will change with distance from the earth's centre. Absolute units avoid the latter complication.

If a system of forces hold a body at rest then the forces are said to be in balance. If the body is in motion the forces are said to be unbalanced.

Example problems:

1. What force in newtons will give a mass of 10 kg an acceleration of 50 cm/sec^2?

Solution: $F = Ma$
$= 10 \times 50 = 500$ Newtons

2. If a stone whose mass is 12 kg falls with an acceleration of 9.8 m per sec^2, what is the unbalanced force exerted on the stone?

Solution: $F = Ma$
$= 12 \times 9.8 = 120$ Newtons

3. If a car weighing 1500 kg is brought to rest from 60 mph in 8.0 seconds, what is the force exerted by the brakes?

Solution: First find the deceleration (negative acceleration)
$v = u + at$
v = final velocity = zero
$u = 60 \text{ mph} = 60 \times \frac{8}{5} \times \frac{1000}{3600} = 26.7$ m per sec.
$a = ?$
$t = 8.0$ sec.
$0 = 26.7 + a \times 8.0$
$a = -3.3$ m per sec^2
or the deceleration is 3.3 m per sec^2

$F = Ma$ Newtons
$= 1500 \times (-3.3) = -4950$ N.
$\therefore$ the braking force is 4950 N.

NEWTON'S THIRD LAW of MOTION

When a cannon is fired, it recoils. The projectile moves in one direction, the cannon in the opposite direction.

Inside a rocket the expanding (burning) gases push against the rocket moving it forward and the rocket pushes against the gases moving them rearward.

A person standing on the floor exerts a force against it while the floor exerts an equal and opposite force against the person.

In all cases the forces acting are equal and opposite. Newtons third law states that to every action (force) there is an equal and opposite reaction (force).

NEWTON'S LAW of UNIVERSAL GRAVITATION

Newton proved that all bodies exert forces of attraction on one another. An apple falls because the earth exerts an attracting force on it. The apple also exerts an attracting force on the earth but it is as small in comparison as the mass of the apple is to the mass of the earth. It is the force of attraction (gravity) of the sun that keeps the planets in their orbits just as the earth's gravitational force keeps the moon in orbit.

The greater the distance between bodies, the smaller is the gravitational force; the greater their masses, the greater is the attracting force. These facts constitute Newtons law of gravitation: the force of attraction between two bodies is proportional to their masses and inversely proportional to the distance between their centres.

WORK ENERGY POWER

Work is done on an object only when a force causes the object to move.

Work is defined as Force x Distance

$$W = Fs$$

In the MKS system, F is measured in Newtons, s is measured in meters. Thus work is measured in Newton-meters.

In the CGS system, F is in dynes, s is in cm.
$\therefore$ W is measured in dyne-cm.

In the English system, F is measured in pounds, s is in feet,
$\therefore$ W is measured in Foot-pounds (Ft-lb)

By definition one Newton-meter = 1 Joule
and one dyne-cm = 1 Erg

Since $W = Fs = M \times a \times s = \text{mass} \times \frac{\text{distance}}{\text{sec}^2} \times \text{distance}$

$$= \text{kg} \times \frac{\text{m}^2}{\text{sec}^2} \text{ Joules}$$

$$= 1000 \text{ gm} \times \frac{(100 \text{ cm})^2}{\text{sec}^2}$$

$$= 10000000 \frac{\text{gm cm}^2}{\text{sec}^2} \text{ ergs}$$

$$= 10^7 \text{ ergs}$$

or 1 Joule = 10^7 ergs

Energy is the ability to do work and when work is done, energy is consumed. The units of energy are the same ergs and joules as used in measuring work.

There are two forms of energy: *POTENTIAL and KINETIC.* Potential energy (PE) is that due to the position or condition of a body. The water above a dam possesses PE because of its height; compressed air possesses PE; the storage battery possesses PE in chemical form. Kinetic energy (KE) is energy due to motion. The water flowing over a dam possesses KE because of its motion. The PE of compressed air can be converted to KE by releasing it through a nozzle. The motion of molecules of materials (Kinetic theory of matter) is a form of KE that is directly measurable by the temperature of the materials.

The *Law of Conservation of Energy* states that energy can be converted from one form to another but cannot be destroyed. The work that would be required to raise the water to its highest level in the dam is a measure of the PE it possesses at that point; as it passes down the flumes, its height and therefore its PE decreases, but its speed and hence KE, increases. At the top PE is maximum while KE is zero; at the bottom PE is zero while KE is a maximum. At any intermediate stage the water possesses both PE and KE and the law of conservation of energy states that the total energy, PE + KE, is the same for all such stages.

The law of conservation of energy can be applied to the simple pendulum. The PE of the pendulum at its highest point A, is equivalent to the work done in raising it through the height, h, $\therefore$ PE = W = Fh = Mah

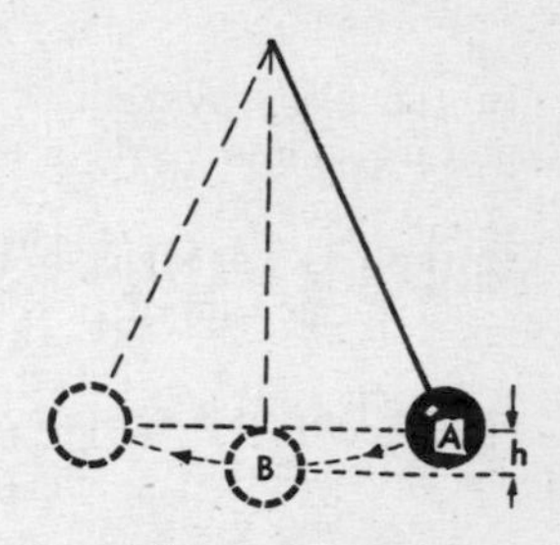

The Pendulum

Since the only acceleration involved is that due to the force of gravity then let a = g = acceleration due to gravity.
$\therefore$ PE at A = Mgh ergs (in C.G.S. units)

When released from A, the pendulum will acquire a velocity v cm. per sec at position B and this velocity will be the same as acquired by falling through the vertical distance, h.

$\therefore$ at B, $v^2 = u^2 + 2as = 0 + 2gh$
$\therefore gh = \frac{1}{2}v^2$

By the law of conservation of energy, the KE at B will equal the PE at A.

$\therefore$ at B KE = Mgh ergs
But $gh = \frac{1}{2}v^2$
$\therefore$ at B KE = $\frac{1}{2}Mv^2$ ergs

This equation is true for any body of mass M gm travelling at a velocity v cm per sec.

Example

A 1 kgm mass falls from rest through a height of 3 meters. What is the KE at the end of its fall? What is the PE at its maximum height (use $g = 980\ cm/sec^2$)?

Solution:

$$KE = Mgh$$
$$= 1000 \times 980 \times 300 = 3 \times 98 \times 10^6$$
$$= 294 \times 10^6 \text{ ergs}$$

And KE at bottom = PE at top = 294×10^6 ergs.

BERNOULLI'S PRINCIPLE

Any fluid at rest such as air on a calm day, exerts a pressure on the surfaces with which it is in contact. This pressure is called *Static Pressure* and it is a form of PE. When in motion the fluid possesses both PE and KE. Bernoulli discovered that as the velocity (KE) of a fluid increased its static pressure (PE) decreased and that this change took place according to the law of energy conservation, that is, KE + PE remained constant. For example, when flowing through a constriction in a pipe, a fluid will speed up so that the same quantity will pass through the smaller section as through the larger. At the constriction (or throat) the higher velocity is accompanied by a higher KE but a lower PE or static pressure. This form of duct is called a Venturi Tube and can be used for measuring fluid flows in pipes by comparing the different pressures.

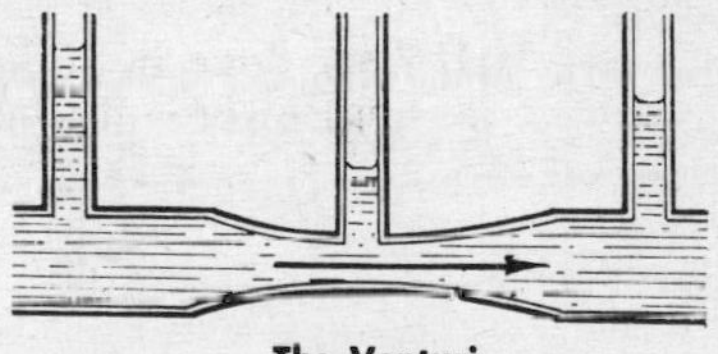

The Venturi

The cross section (airfoil) of an aircraft wing is shaped so that Bernoulli's principle applies to the flow of air over its contours. The upper surface has the greater curvature which means that the air must travel faster over the upper surface (it has farther to go) than over the lower. The result is a lower pressure on the upper surface than on the lower and therefore a net lifting force.

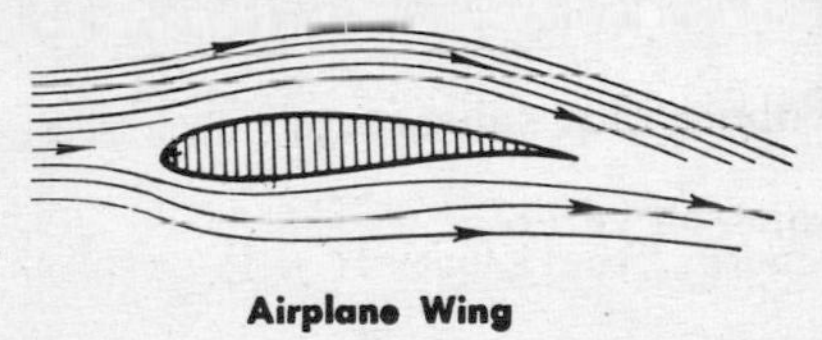

Airplane Wing

POWER

Power is the rate of consuming energy or in other words, the rate of doing work.

Power = Work done per unit of time

$$P = \frac{W}{t}$$

One Joule per second is defined as one Watt and 550 Ft-pd. per sec. is defined as one Horse-power. (HP)

Converting HP to Watts:

1 HP = 550 Ft-pd per second
= 550 × 30.48 × 453.6 × 980 = 746 ergs per sec.
(10^7 ergs = 1 Joule)
∴ 1 HP = 746 joules per sec = 746 watts.

Example Problems:

1. A pump lifts 300 kg of water into a stand pipe 20 meters high — Calculate (i) The work done in joules.

   (ii) What power in Watts and HP would complete this work in 40 seconds?

Solution (i) Work done = Fs = M × a × s (here a = g)
= 300 × 9.8 × 20 = 58,800 Joules

(ii) Work done in 40 seconds = 58,800 joules

$$\therefore \text{Power} = \frac{W}{t} = \frac{58{,}800}{40} = 1470 \text{ Watts}$$

$$= \frac{1470}{746} = 2 \text{ HP. (approx.)}$$

ARCHIMEDES' PRINCIPLE

THE LAW of FLOTATION

Density is the mass of a unit volume of a substance.

$$D = \frac{M}{V}$$ gm/cc, lb/cu ft; tons/cu yd etc.

Specific Gravity is the number of times heavier a material is than water when equal volumes are considered.

$$\text{S.G.} = \frac{\text{mass of any volume of a substance}}{\text{mass of an equal volume of water}}$$

or $S.G. = \dfrac{\text{Density of the substance}}{\text{Density of water}}$

S.G. is simply a ratio or comparison, it has no units.

Archimede's Principle states that when submerged in a fluid (liquid or gas), the apparent loss of weight of a body is equal to the weight of the fluid displaced by the body. The simple experiment illustrated in the drawing will verify Archimedes Principle.

150 gm. 30 gm. water 120 gm.

S.G. of Solids and Liquids by Arch. Princ.

1. Solids

The following example readings and calculations will suggest an experiment to determine the S.G. of solids denser than water.

Weight of solid in air	= 20 gm
Weight of solid while submerged in water	= 15 gm
Apparent loss in wt.	= 5 gm
Wt. of water displaced (by Arch. Pr.)	= 5 gm
Volume of object = vol. displaced water	= 5 cc

$\therefore S.G. = \dfrac{\text{wt. of object}}{\text{wt. of equal vol. water}} = \dfrac{20}{5} = 4$

2. Liquids

The following will suggest an experiment to determine the S.G. of a liquid using Arch. Princ.

Weight of any solid (denser than water) in air	= 20 gm
Weight of the object in water	= 15 gm
Weight of the object in the liquid	= 16 gm

Since the same object is used throughout, then the volumes of water and liquid displaced will be equal and the weight of each quantity displaced will equal the apparent loss of wt. of the object. So we have the weights of equal volumes of the liquid and water to compare.

Wt. of water displaced	= 5 gm
Wt. of liquid displaced	= 4 gm

$S.G. = \dfrac{\text{wt. of liquid displaced}}{\text{wt. of water displaced}} = \dfrac{4}{5} = 0.8$

Law of Flotation

The weight of a floating object is equal to the weight of the fluid (liquid or gas) it displaces. This principle is easily verified experimentally as indicated in the illustration.

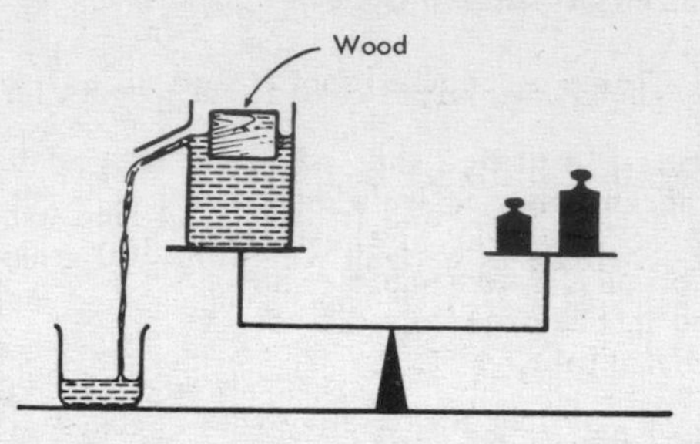

The magnitude of the buoyant force that a fluid exerts on a body immersed in it is exactly equal to the weight of the fluid displaced by the body. A balloon filled with a gas that is lighter than air, such as helium, displaces a weight of air greater than its own weight and therefore experiences a net upward force causing it to rise. The buoyancy of a submarine can be controlled by taking water aboard in ballast tanks or by expelling water from the tanks with compressed air, thus the depth can be regulated even without the combination of forward motion and horizontal "fin" control.

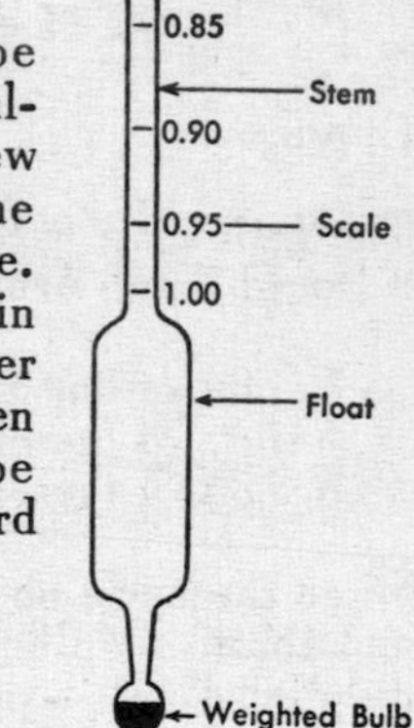

The Hydrometer

In certain industries the S.G. of liquids must be known; milk, brine for preserving pickles, sulphuric acid in storage cells and alcohol are a few examples. The hydrometer, which is based on the principle of flotation, is used for this purpose. The greater the S.G. of the liquid the higher in the liquid the hydrometer will float and the lower the S.G. the deeper it will float. The scale then can be marked to read S.G. directly and it will be noted that the scale decreases in the upward direction.

Problems - S.G. and Density

1. The specific gravity of pure milk is 1.09. What is the density of a mixture containing 500 c.c.s of milk and 100 c.c.s of water?

Solution:

1 c.c. of water weighs 1 grm. $\therefore$ 100 c.c.s of water weigh 100 grms.
1 c.c. of milk weighs 1.09 gr. $\therefore$ 100 c.c.s of milk weigh 109 grms.
$\therefore$ 500 c.c.s of milk weigh 545 grms.
$\therefore$ 100 c.c.s of water + 500 c.c.s of milk weigh 645 grms.

600 c.c.s of the mixture weigh 645 grms.

$\therefore$ 1 c.c. of the mixture weighs $\frac{645}{600}$ grms. = 1.075 grms.

$\therefore$ The density of the mixture is 1.075 grms/c.c.

2. An alloy contains platinum and iridium in the proportion 7:3. If platinum has a S.G. 21.5, and iridium 22.4 find (a) The S.G. of the alloy, (b) The volume of a lump weighing 100 grms.

Solution:

(a) In every 10 c.c.s of alloy, there are 7 c.c.s platinum + 3 c.c.s iridium.

1 c.c. platinum weighs 21.5 grms.
$\therefore$ 7 c.c. " " 150.5 grms.

1 c.c. iridium weighs 22.4 grms.
$\therefore$ 3 c.c.s " " 67.2 grms.

$\therefore$ 10 c.c.s of the alloy weigh 150.5 + 67.2 grms. = 217.7 grms.
$\therefore$ 1 c.c. of the alloy weighs 21.77 grms.
i.e. its S.G. is 21.77

(b) 21.77 grms occupy 1 c.c.
$\therefore$ 100 grms occupy $\frac{100}{21.77}$ c.c.s = 4.6 c.c.s

3. A lump of metal of S.G. 9 weighs 36 grms. What will it seem to weigh when submerged (a) in water, (b) in oil of S.G. 0.5?

Solution:

Mass = 36 grms.
Density = 9 grms/c.c.

$\frac{\text{Mass}}{\text{Volume}}$ = density

$\frac{36}{V}$ = 9

V = $\frac{36}{9}$ = 4 c.c.s

i.e. 4 c.c.s of water are displaced
4 c.c.s of water weigh 4 grms.

i.e. The buoyant force = 4 grms.
Mass of the metal in water
= Mass in air – upthrust
= 36 – 4 = 32 grms.

4 c.c.s of liquid oil are displaced
4 c.c.s of oil weigh 4×0.5 gm. = 2 gms.

i.e. the buoyant force of the oil = 2 gms.

Mass of the metal in oil = 36–2 gms = 34 grms.

Unit 2 VIBRATIONS

WAVE MOTION

Transmission of energy by waves.

Particles in the vicinity of a disturbance in a medium will vibrate and because of friction or an elastic bond between them the particles will transmit the disturbance particle to particle throughout the medium. Energy can thus travel great distances through media though the particles of the media do not themselves move far from their points of rest. Some particles at certain distances apart, vibrate with the same frequency and amplitude, in the same direction (in phase), others in opposite directions (out of phase).

There are three types of vibrations, transverse, longitudinal and torsional. Transverse vibrations are performed by the tuning fork, stretched strings and the pendulum i.e., the particles vibrate *across* the axis of the object. A weight at the end of an elastic band or coiled spring suspended vertically, will perform longitudinal vibrations e.g., *along* the length of the axis of the body. A weight suspended on the end of a steel wire will undergo torsional vibrations when rotated and released. The motion causes a to-and-fro twisting action in the wire.

The *amplitude* is the maximum distance a vibrating body travels from its point of rest in one direction.

One *cycle* or one vibration, is performed when the body moves to its full amplitude on one side across to its full amplitude on the other side and back to rest.

The *period* of a vibration is the time in seconds required to complete one cycle.

The *frequency* of a vibrating object is the number of vibrations per second that it performs.

The *wave length* is the shortest distance between two consecutive particles in the same phase.

The Wave Equation

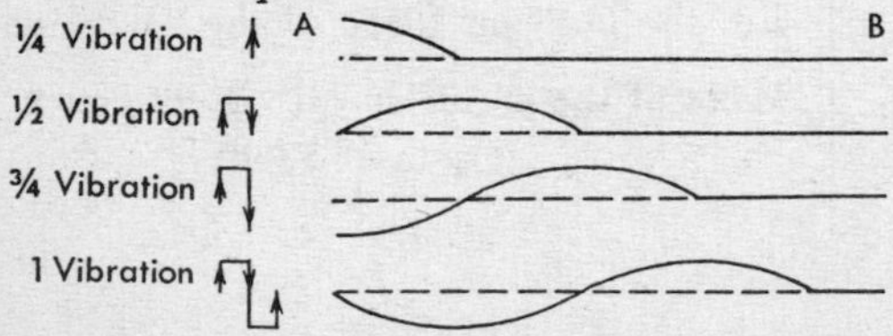

Let A be the point of disturbance (a regular vibration) in a rope of any length and of which A B represents the rest position. During the first quarter of a vibration the disturbance travels to position C, each particle in the string moving downward because of the energy transmitted by the previous particle. When the disturbance returns to its rest position at A, it has completed one half a cycle and the particles between A and C are moving towards their rest position while those between C and D are moving away. As the disturbance completes its third and fourth quarters of its cycle, the particles along the rope will move in the directions indicated by the small arrows and the rope will have completed one full wave lengh. Although the wave travels the length of the rope the particles move only vertically (transverse vibrations).

Let the frequency of the disturbance be n v.p.s. and the wave length be λ (lambda) feet.

During	1	cycle	the disturbance	travels	$1 \times \lambda$ feet
"	2	"	" "	"	$2 \times \lambda$ "
"	3	"	" "	"	$3 \times \lambda$ "
"	n	"	" "	"	$n \times \lambda$ "

Since n is measured in vibrations per second, then $n \times \lambda$ represents the number of feet travelled per second, e.g. velocity of the wave.

$$\therefore V = n\lambda$$

Example:

1. If the frequency of a disturbance is 250 v.p.s. and the wave length is 4 feet what is the velocity of the wave?

Solution:

$$V = n\lambda = 250 \times 4 = 1000 \text{ f.p.s.}$$

2. What frequency will produce a wave length of 11 meters and velocity of 330 m.p.s.?

Solution:

$$n = V/\lambda = \frac{330}{11} = 30 \text{ v.p.s.}$$

Interference in Waves.

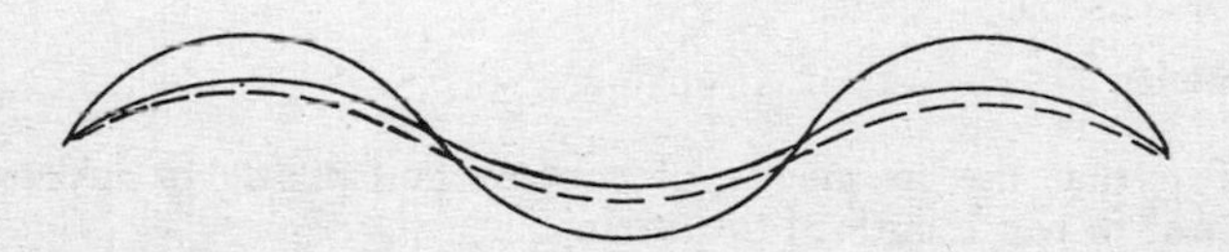

If two wave disturbances act simultaneously in a medium, (e.g. a rope) the resulting disturbance of the particles is the algebraic sum of the two disturbances.

If curve 1 and curve 2 represent the two wave-trains in which λ_2 = 2 x $_1$, then curve 3 represents the resulting motion. A particle normally at a is subjected to the two disturbances represented by ab and ac. The actual displacement is represented, therefore by ad (= ab + ac). Similarly Bf represents the displacement of the particle normally at B (Bf = Bf + 0) and hk represents the displacement of the particle normally at h (kh = hm + (- hg)).

Standing Waves are a special case of wave interference. They are produced for example, in a single string when two identical waves travel in opposite directions. Standing waves can readily be produced in a long rope tied to a fixed point at one end while the other end is oscilated up and down (the disturbance) regularly. A wave train will travel away from the moving end, be reflected from the fixed end to create an identical wave train travelling in the opposite direction to the original. A pattern of loops and nodes which appear to be stationary will develop.

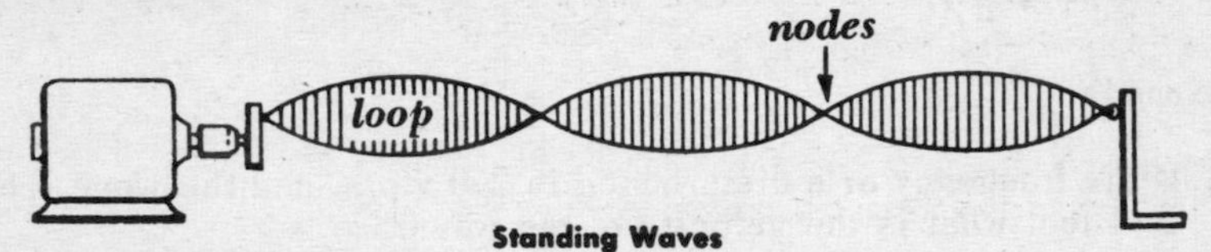

Standing Waves

The nodes occur when crests and troughs of the original and reflected waves coincide, the waves cancel each other's motion. The loops are the results of crests coinciding with crests and troughs with troughs; they tend to reinforce each other and increase the amplitude.

SOUND

Recall that sound is produced by rapidly vibrating bodies and requires a medium for its propogation (transmission). Sound waves are always longitudinal and each wave consists of one rarefaction and one condensation. The wave formula, $V = n\lambda$ applies also to sound.

Experiment

To show that the frequency of a stretched string is inversely proportional to the length of the string.

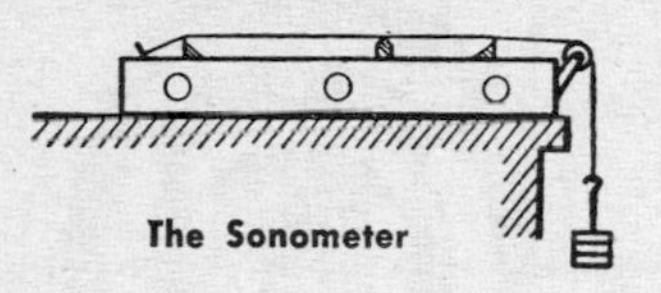

Two strings on a sonometer are adjusted by means of their tension to produce the same pitch. A moveable bridge is placed at the ½, ¼, ⅓ point of one of the strings while the pitch for each fraction of the string is compared with the full length string or some tuning forks. It should be found that

½ the length produces 2 x n of the full length

¼ the length produces 4 x n of the full length

⅓ the length produces 3 x n of the full length, etc.

Thus the frequency of a stretched string is inversely proportional to its length.

Tension is another factor effecting the frequency of a vibrating string: frequency becomes higher when the tension is increased.

Also *diameter* is a factor: a thick string vibrates slowly; and density: a heavy string vibrates slowly.

Interference in Sound Waves.

If two tuning forks of slightly different frequencies are sounded together, periodic changes in the intensity of the combined sounds are noticeable. These changes (regular) are called beats and can be explained with reference to the diagram below.

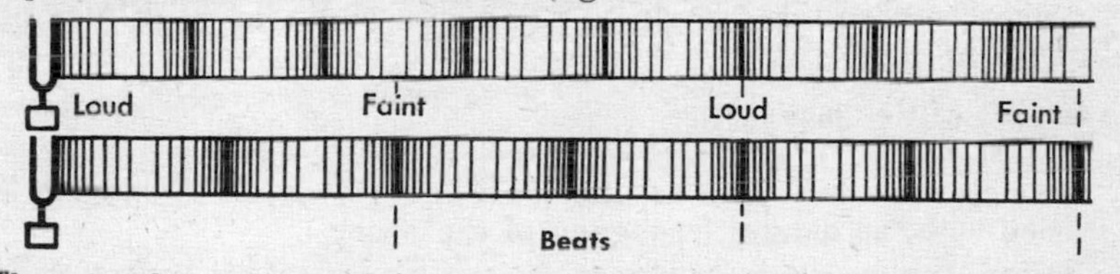

When condensations of each wave train coincide (or when rarefactions of each coincide) they reinforce each other to create maximum intensity. When a rarefaction of one wave coincides with a condensation of the other they partially cancel each other to create a minimum intensity (compare with loops and nodes of a standing transverse wave). The number of beats (one beat = 1 loud + 1 faint sound) is equal to the difference in the frequencies of the two sources.

Complete interference will be observed when rotating a sounding tuning fork near the ear. In four positions which appear to be in line with each corner of the fork, the sound is almost inaudible while in all other positions it is normal. With reference to drawing, as the prongs move inwardly a condensation is formed between them (C). At this same instant rarefactions (R) are produced on the outer faces of the prongs. Previous oscillations form the alternating pattern shown. Along the lines moving out from the 4 corners of the fork condensations and rarefactions coincide and cancel each other with the result that the sound is at a minimum.

Two amplifier speakers can produce similar patterns in an auditorium, hence "dead spots" may arise in various locations.

Resonance

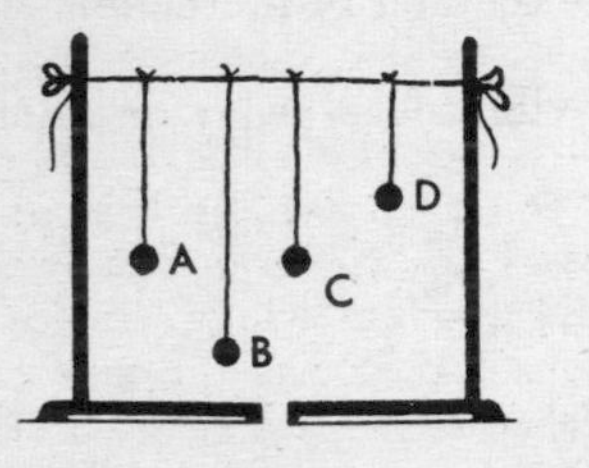

Pendulums suspended on a string as shown will demonstrate resonance nicely. If B or D are set in vibration they have no definite effect if any, on the others. If all are first stopped and A only is put in motion, then C will soon join in of its own accord and begin to vibrate regularly. This occurs because C and A, being of the same length, have the same natural frequency. C is said to undergo sympathetic vibrations in resonance with A. If one object is vibrating, even with small amplitude, a second object of the same natural frequency in its neighbourhood may begin to vibrate in sympathy and often with larger amplitude.

Examples of Resonance

1. A small child may push another in a heavy swing if the pushes are timed with the natural frequency of the swing.

2. A car can often be "unstuck" if it is rocked back and forth with pushes of the same frequency as its natural rocking motion.

3. Soldiers marching on a bridge are told to break step – why?

4. A singer may shatter fine crystalware with his voice – how?

Experiment to illustrate sympathetic vibrations

Two tuning forks of the same frequency and mounted on resonance boxes are set facing each other as shown. One of them is struck solidly and then stopped vibrating by grasping with the hand. The second will now be vibrating. Energy from the struck fork was transmitted to the second of the same natural frequency, causing it to vibrate in resonance.

To illustrate sympathetic vibrations, using identical tuning-forks.

Experiment to illustrate resonance in air columns.

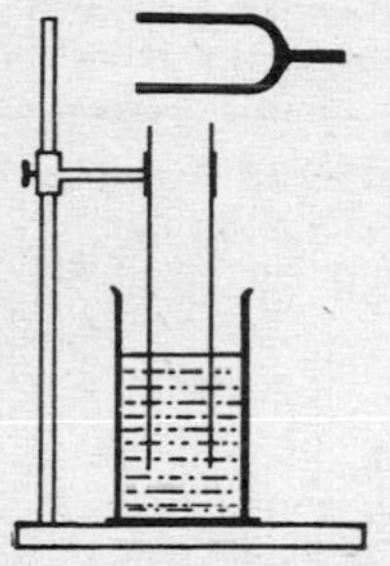

A metal or glass tube about two inches in diameter is held in a cylinder of water as shown. A sounding tuning fork is held over the open end of the tube. The tube is now raised and lowered until a maximum intensity of sound is heard. At this point the *air column* in the tube is resonating with the fork. In other words, *at a particular length* the air column has the same natural frequency as the fork. By further experimentation it will be found that the higher the frequency of the fork, the shorter is the length of the air column that resonates with it. To explain this phenomena, consider the lower prong of the fork. As it moves downward it sends a condensation down the tube, this condensation is reflected by the water and returns to the position of the prong just as the prong is sending a condensation outward from the tube. Thus the two condensations coincide to produce maximum sound intensity on their outward journey.

Many wind instruments employ the principle of resonance in air columns. The organ pipe, flute, clarinet, saxophone, oboe and many others use a vibrating reed to set the air column vibrating in resonance and the pitch is varied by opening and closing holes in the pipe to vary its length.

LIGHT

Light is a form of energy the nature of which is not yet fully known. It generally travels in straight lines (is rectilinear), can travel in a vacuum, and is a transverse wave form of energy of extremely high frequency (10^{15} c.p.s.) and small amplitude; it originates in the motion of electrons within atoms of materials.

Reflection in Plane Mirrors – Review

The accompanying drawing will help recall the important points about reflection in plane mirrors:

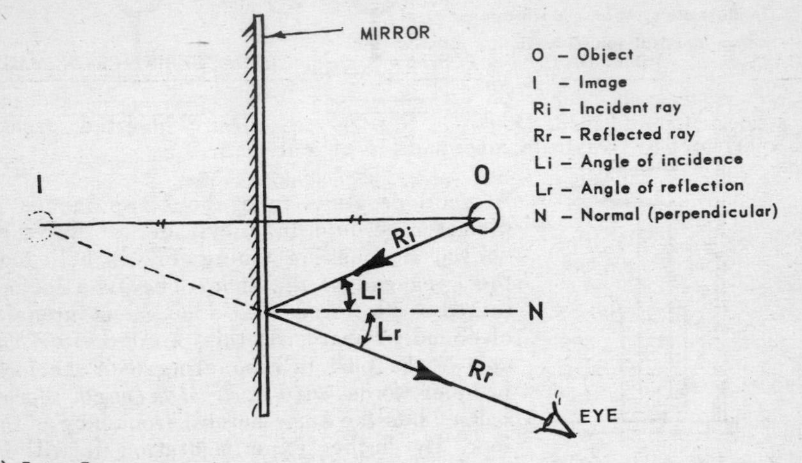

(a) Li = Lr
(b) The Ri, Rr and N all lie in the same plane
(c) The line IO cuts the mirror at right angles and is bisected by the mirror
(d) The image is virtual (imaginary), the same size as the object and is laterally inverted (sides are reversed)

Observations (a) and (b) are known as the laws of reflection and are true for all cases of reflection. The characteristics of images in plane mirrors are stated in observation (d).

Reflection in Curved Mirrors

Experiment to study the images produced by a concave mirror.

Apparatus:

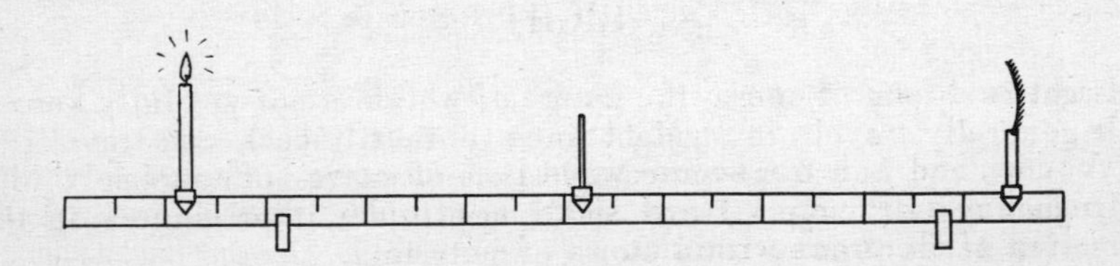

The focal length (F) of the mirror is found by focusing some distant object (e.g. windows at end of long corridor) on a small screen and measuring the distance between the screen and the mirror.

The mirror is then placed on the optical bench and the candle (object) is located at various positions, (distances from mirror measured as multiples of F).

CASE	OBJECT POSITION	IMAGE POSITION	CHARACTERISTICS OF IMAGE		
1.	beyond 2F	between F & 2F	smaller,	inverted,	real
2.	at 2F	at 2F	same size,	"	"
3.	between F and 2F	beyond 2F	larger,	"	"
4.	at F	no image	–	–	–
5.	between F and mirror	behind mirror	larger,	erect,	virtual

Locating Images by Diagram

Points to remember:

(1) All rays parallel to P.A. are reflected through P.F.

(2) All rays through CC are reflected back along themselves.

(3) The image of a point on the object is found at the intersection of the reflected rays from this point.

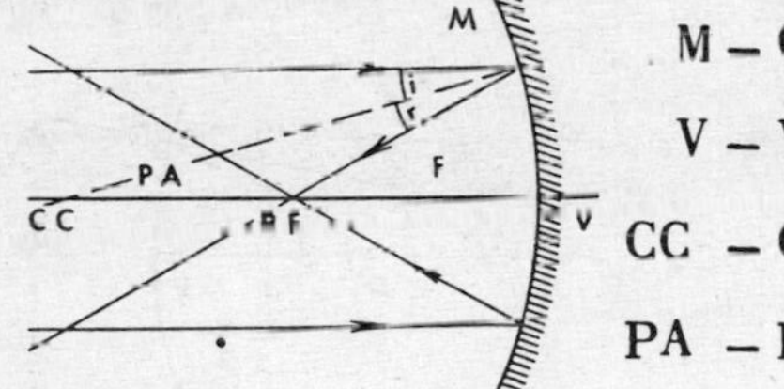

M – Concave mirror

V – Vertex of mirror

CC – Centre of curvature

PA – Principle Axis

Examples:

1. Locate the images diagramatically for cases 1, 3 and 5 of the above experiment. Compare the results of the drawing with those in the table of observations.

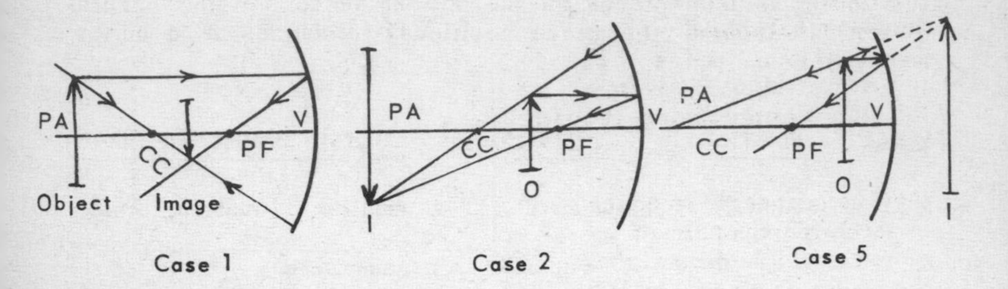

How the eye sees the image

The eye catches a cone of rays through the image tip, formed by reflection from the mirror

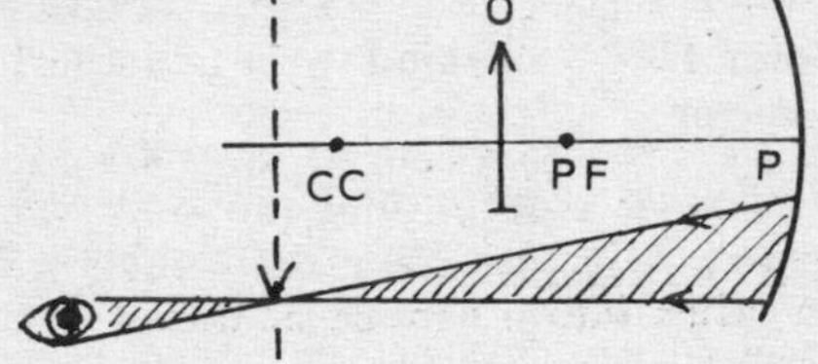

But this cone of rays, actually came from the tip of the object. Thus:

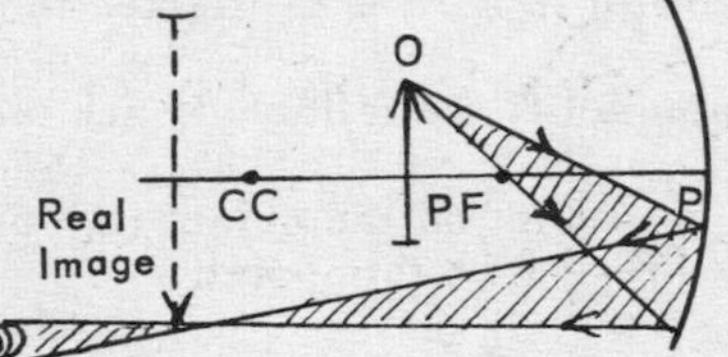

Similarly:

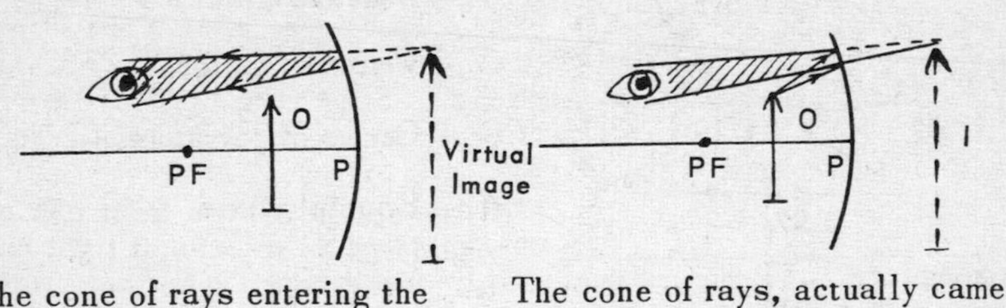

The cone of rays entering the eye enables it to see the image tip. This rays diverge and seem to come from the image tip.

The cone of rays, actually came from the tip of the object.

Refraction

The accompanying drawing will help recall an experiment in which refraction of light through a glass plate was studied. It was found

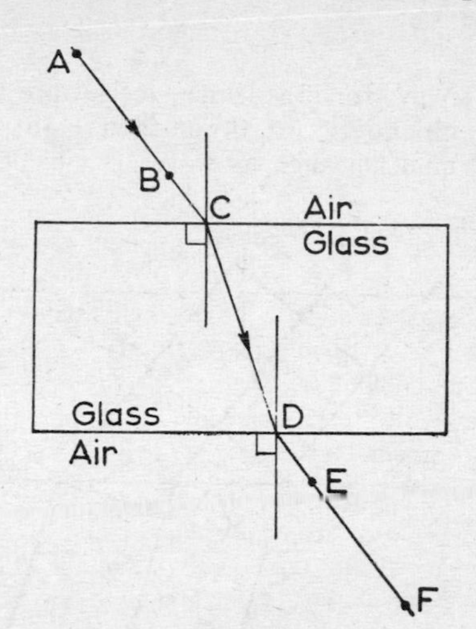

that:

(a) the ray is bent towards the normal on entering the glass

(b) the ray is bent away from the normal on leaving the glass

(c) the emergent angle is equal to the original angle of incidence which means that the emergent ray is parallel to the incident ray.

Explanation of refraction.

As with sound, light is propogated in all directions from its source to form spherical wave fronts.

If we take a set of waves far enough away from the source that the rays are parallel (as we receive from the sun) then we can use such a beam of rays to explain refraction or bending of light rays as they pass from one medium into a denser medium.

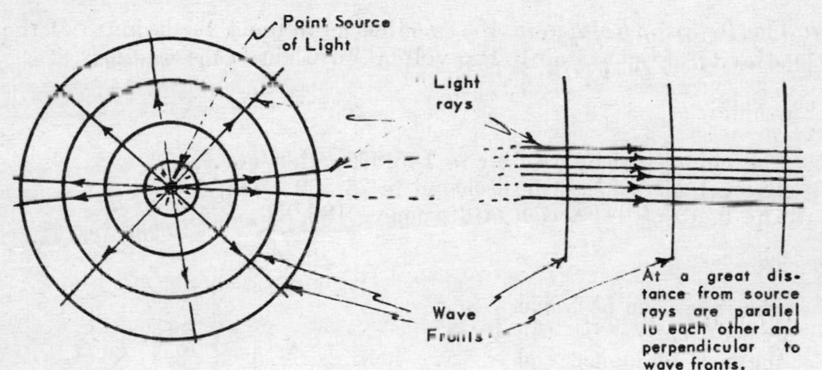

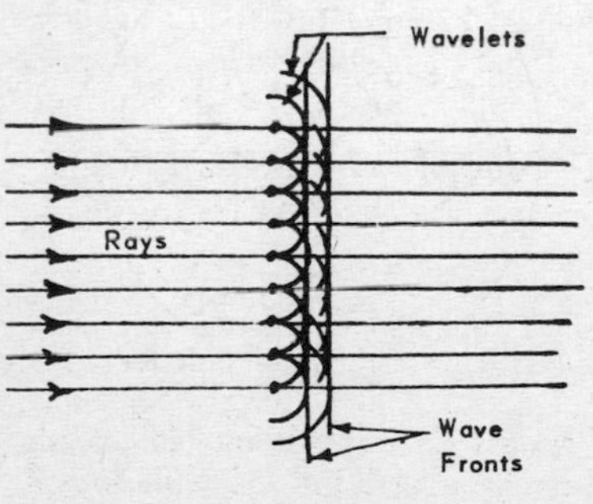

All points on a wave front can be considered as sources of light and will send out spherical wave fronts of their own which we shall call wavelets. The outer edge of the wavelets combine to form wave fronts as shown, while the intersecting wavelets tend to cancel each other. Note that the rays are always perpendicular to wave fronts as are radii to the surface of a sphere.

Now, for simplicity, let's take three rays of a beam and direct them obliquely (at other than right angles) to the surface of a denser medium such as water.

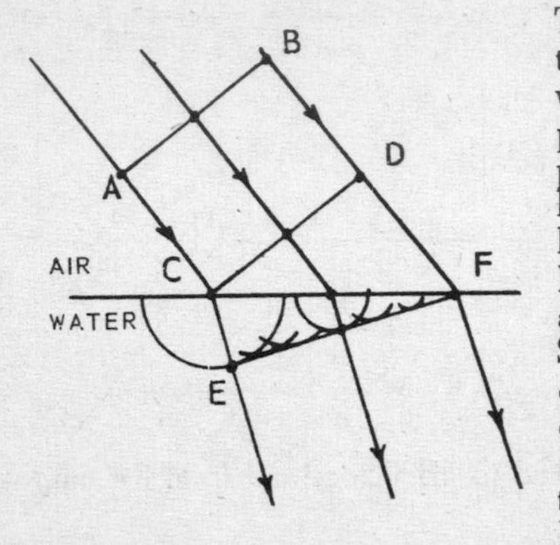

The denser medium will reduce the velocity of the light. As the wave front AB travels forward, the point A will strike the water at point C at the same time as point B reaches its new position D. Now B will act as a point source of light and will send out wavelets at a reduced speed in the water. Similarly, wavelets will be sent out in succession along CF as each point on the wave front CD strikes the water. In the time it takes point D to travel the distance DF, a wavelet from C travels a shorter distance CE. The successive wavelets produced from points along CF combine to form a new wave front, EF, travelling through the water in a different direction from that of the original incident beam.

The *Index of Refraction* of a medium is defined as the ratio of the velocity of light in air to the velocity of light in the medium.

Example:

The velocity of light in air is 186,000 miles/sec.
The velocity of light in diamond is 75,300 miles/sec.
$\therefore$ The Index of Refraction of diamond $= \frac{186,000}{75,300} = 2.47$

The index can be found geometrically if the angle of incidence and angle of refraction are known.

Example: Find the index of refraction of quartz if the ∠i of a ray of light passing from air into the quartz is 59° and its ∠r = 30°.

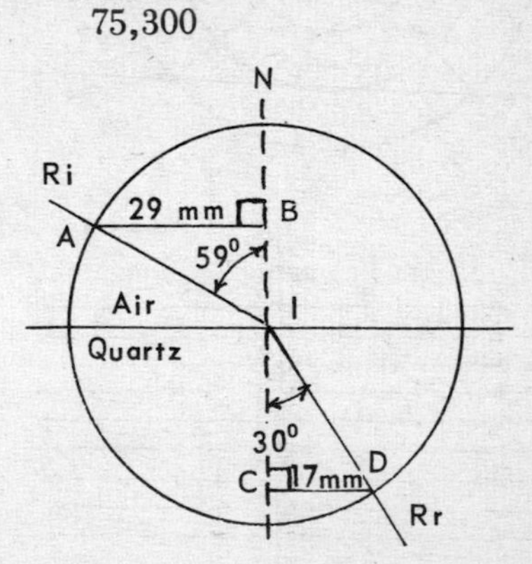

Solution:

(1) Construct the boundry, N, Li, Lr as shown

(2) With centre the point I and suitable radius, draw a circle cutting Ri at A and Rr at D. Draw perpendiculars from A and D to the normal at B and C.

(3) Measure the lengths of AB and CD in mm.

(4) The index of refraction $= \frac{AB}{CD} = \frac{29 \text{ mm}}{17 \text{ mm}} = 1.7$

The Critical Angle and Total Reflection are shown in the following drawing. When a ray of light passes into a *denser* medium it is always refracted *towards* the normal; thus, for all angles of incidence between 0 and 90°, some refraction occurs. However, when a ray passes from one medium to a *less dense* medium refraction is *away* from the normal. At *a particular angle of incidence – the critical angle* – the emergent ray lies along the boundary between the materials, that is, the refracted angle is 90°. Beyond the critical angle the ray will be completely reflected within the denser medium. For example the critical angle for diamond is about 30° (for water about 43°). Thus a light ray within a diamond will be totally reflected many times internally and as a result the diamond appears to have brilliance.

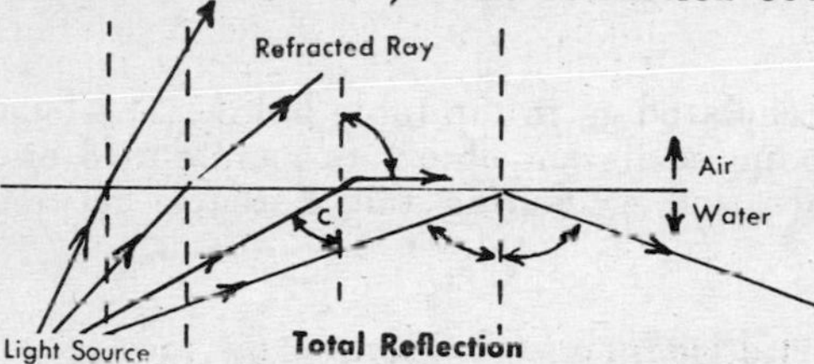

Lenses:

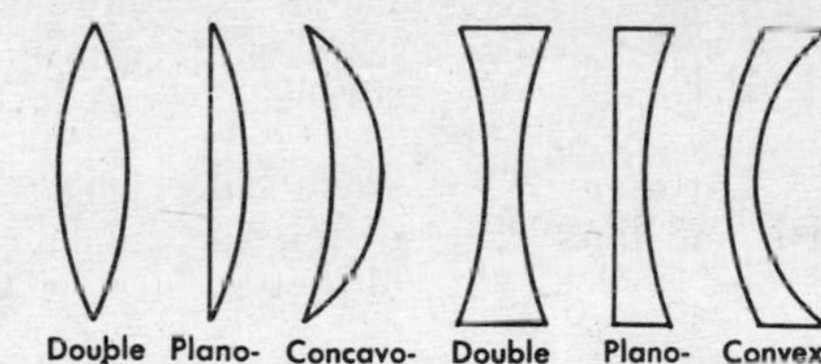

Refraction of rays by lenses:

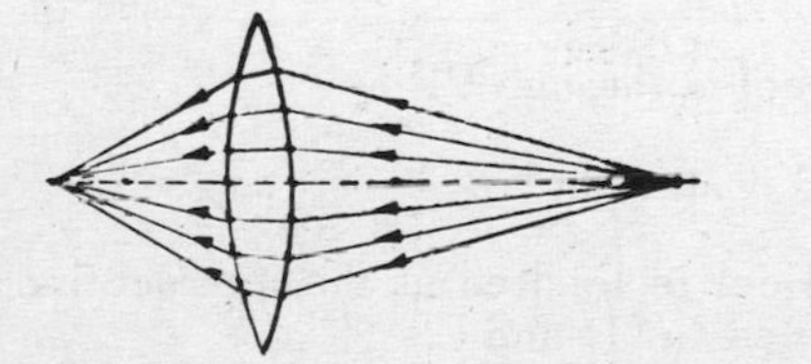

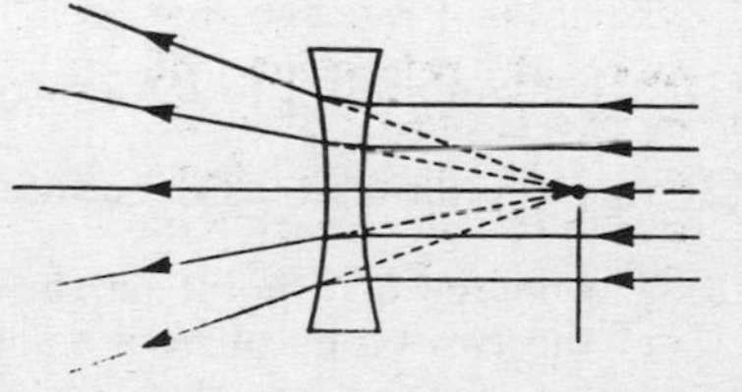

In convex lenses:
Parallel rays are converged through the Principle Focus (PF)

In concave lenses:
Parallel rays are diverged, if produced back through lens they will intersect on PF.

An experiment to study images in a convex lens can be conducted similar to that for a concave mirror.

Apparatus:

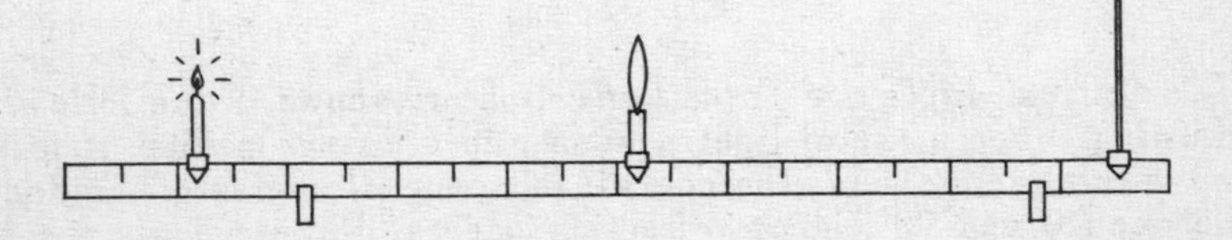

The observations can be tabulated as in the table below. The focal length F is found by focusing a distant object (a candle at 3 or 4 meters) on a small screen and measuring the distance between screen and lens.

CASE	OBJECT POSITION	IMAGE POSITION	IMAGE CHARACTERISTICS
1.	2 meters or more	P.F.	Real, inverted, smaller
2.	2 F	2 F	real, inverted, same size
3.	P.F.	none	– – –
4.	between PF and lens	same side of lens as object	virtual, erect, larger

Locating images in lenses geometrically

Points to remember:

(1) All rays parallel to PA are refracted through PF

(2) Any ray through 0 is considered a straight line

(3) The image of a point on the object is located at the intersection of the two types of rays mentioned in (1) and (2)

Examples:

1. Locate the images geometrically for cases 2 and 4 in the above experiment.

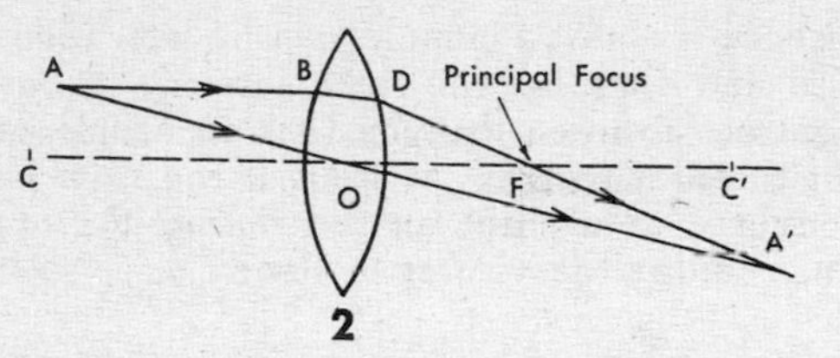

2. Locate the image in a concave lens for

   (a) an object at 2 F

   (b) an object between PF and O

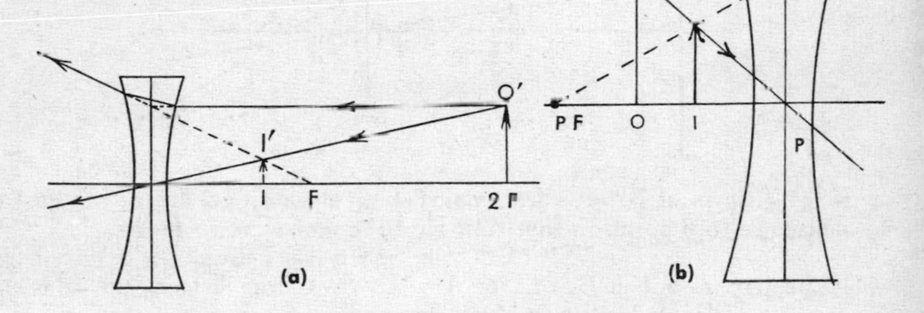

Note: The image in a concave lens is always smaller, erect and virtual.

Some Applications of Refraction

A comparison of parts of the camera and equivalent parts of the human eye:

A Camera	The Human Eye
1. Shutter	1. Eyelid
2. Diaphragm	2. Iris
3. Aperture	3. Pupil
4. Convex lens system	4. Lens
5. Bellows	5. Ciliary muscles
6. Light tight box	6. Sclerotic, Choraid
7. Film	7. Retina

In the Camera, if light from any point of the object is brought to a point focus on the film, a clear image will be obtained when the film is developed. The light entering the aperture is controlled by the *diaphragm*.

In the eye, the Iris, a circular coloured muscle can be extended to close the aperture or *pupil* and diminish the light entering the eye, as on a bright day; or contract to open the pupil as on a dull day, and permit maximum light to enter (reflex action). If the rays from a point on the object converge to a point on the *retina*, the optic nerve related to the brain, enables the viewer to "see".

Action of a camera

The image is small, inverted, real.

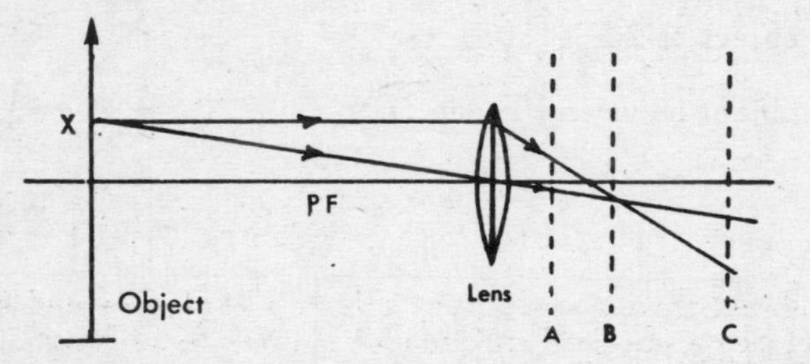

If the film is at B, rays from point X on the object, are refracted to converge to a point on the film. i.e. the image is in focus.

If the film is not at B, e.g. at A or C, rays from X meet the film as a patch of light, to give a blurred image.

Focusing is effected by altering the distance between the object and the camera; or, in a camera of the bellows type, adjusting the distance between the lens and the film, until condition B is obtained.

Action of the human eye

If a person tries to see an object, and the distance between object and eye is fixed, the curvature and hence power of the eye lens is adjusted by extension or contraction of the ciliary muscles to which the lens is attached.

(1) *Normal eye.* This has the full power of accommodation, i.e. for all positions of the object from great distances to approx. 25 cm., the power and focal length of the lens alters, so that rays from a point on the object converge to a point on the retina.

Eye relaxed – Distant Object

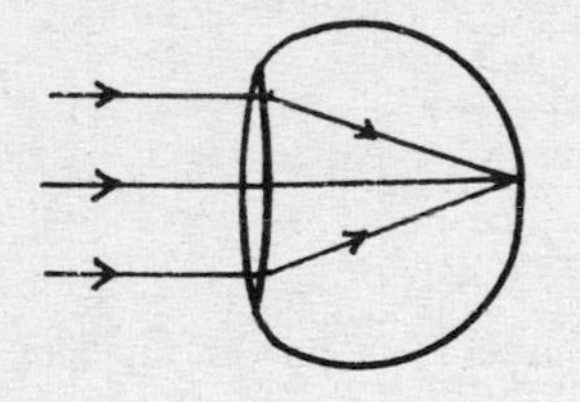

Near Object

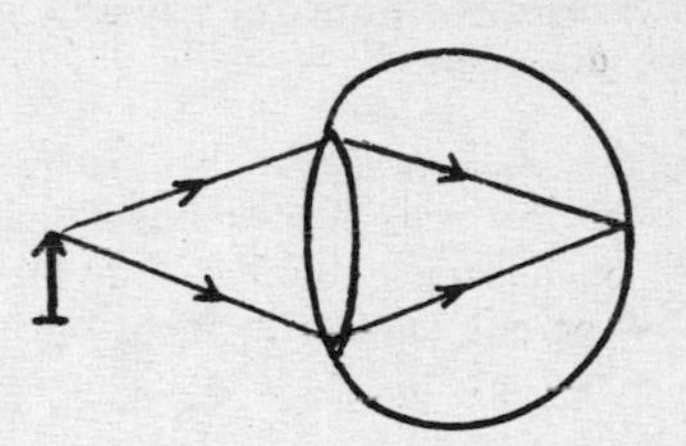

Very near object

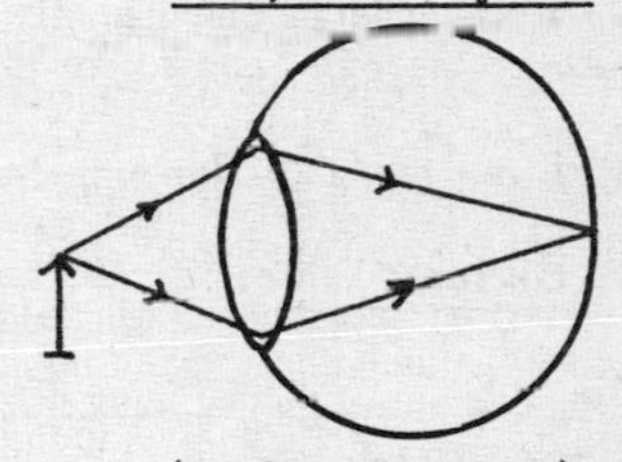

(reading distance)

Eye lens is elongated, and the controlling ciliary muscles are relaxed. Rays from a point on a distant object are almost parallel, and are brought to a focus on the *yellow spot* or most sensitive part of the retina.

As the object moves nearer, the ciliary muscles extend so that the lens becomes more powerful and of shorter focal length. The rays from a point on the object that *can* enter the eye are more diverging, but can still be brought to a focus on the retina.

(2) *Short sight or Myopia* (distant objects are not clearly seen)

Very near object

Further object

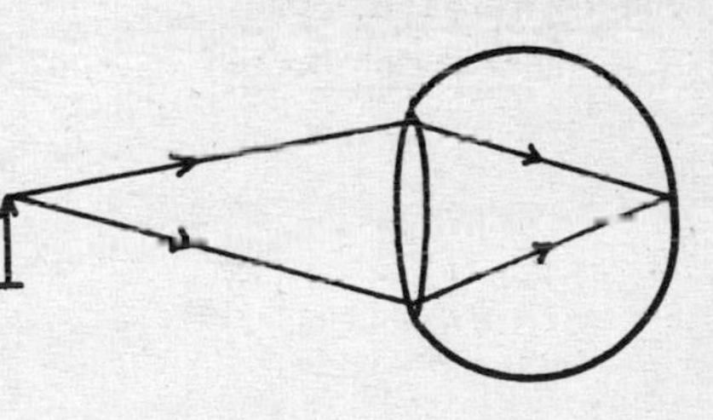

(a)

(b)

The lens becomes less powerful as the distance between the eye and object increases, since the rays that enter it are less diverging than previously.

Object very far away

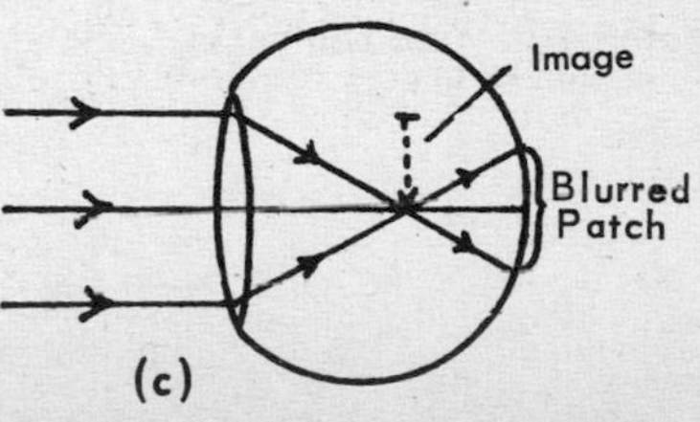

(c)

The lens cannot be further extended (usually the ciliary muscles have reacted the limit of their contraction) and is as in (b) i.e. *too powerful* for parallel rays, which converge within the eyeball.

To correct (c) the eye lens must be made less powerful, i.e. concave spectacles are used.

These *diverge* the parallel rays from a distant object, so that they enter the eye lens as in position (b).

(3) *Long sight or Hypermetrapia* (near objects are not clearly seen)

Distant Object

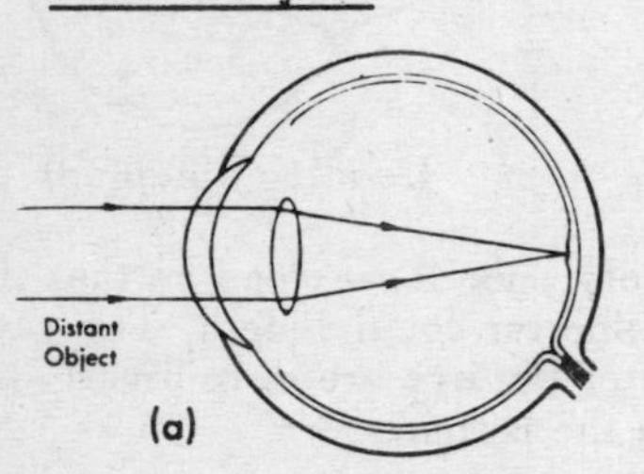

Nearer Object

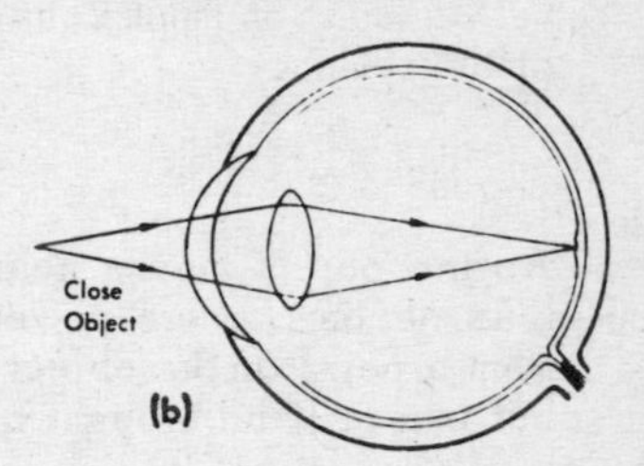

The lens becomes more powerful as the distance between the eye and object decreases, since the rays that enter it are more diverging.

Object within the normal near vision range

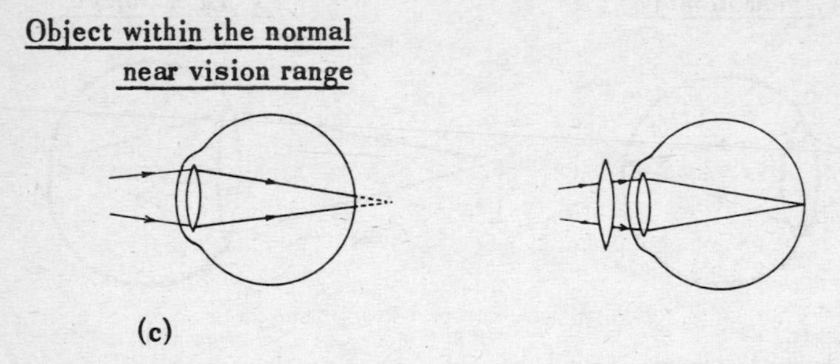

The lens is as powerful as it can be, and the ciliary muscles are in their most extended state. But the lens is of too great a focal length to bring rays to a focus on the retina. The image would be formed *beyond* the retina.

To correct (c) the eye lens must be made more powerful i.e. convex spectacles are used. These converge the rays from near objects slightly, so that they enter the lens as in position (b).

The simple Microscope is a single convex lens used to magnify an object as in case 4 of the experiment on lenses. The image is erect, virtual and larger.

The compound Microscope uses a second (or more) lens to magnify the image of the first lens.

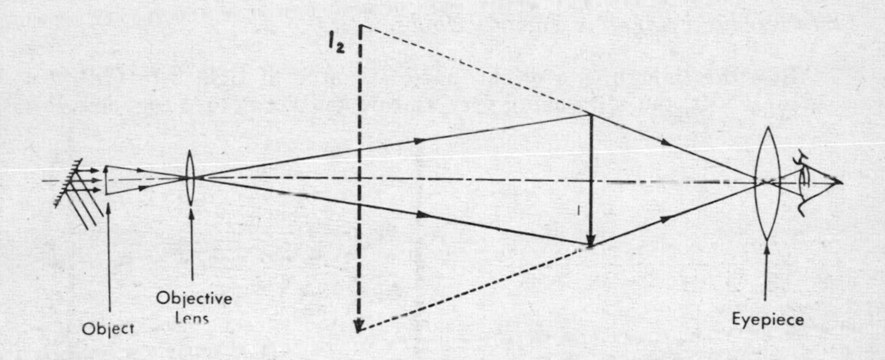

The prism binoculars utilize lenses and *total reflection* in glass prisms. The magnifying power of a telescope depends largely on its length. By means of total reflection, the prism can be used to make light travel several lengths of a shorter instrument. Thus in effect "folding" the telescope to a more convenient size.

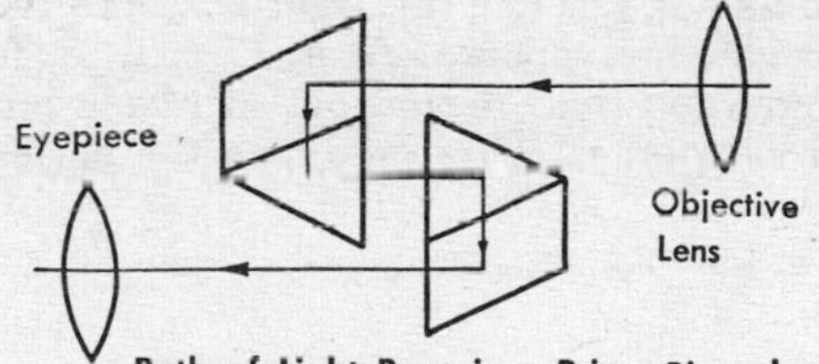

Path of Light Rays in a Prism Binocular

Interference in Light Waves

Spreading of Light from a Narrow Slit

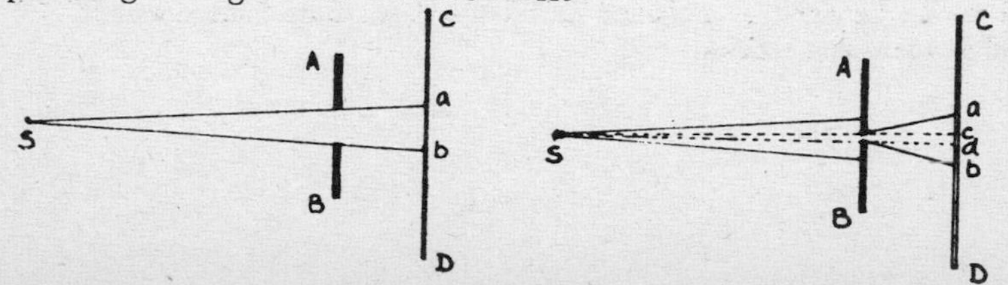

If a narrow source of light S is placed a few feet from an adjustable slit AB and the resultant illumination allowed to fall on a screen CD, it will be observed that:–

(a) when the slit is wide (2 or 3mm.) the patch of light ab is of a width consistent with the propagation of light in straight lines.

(b) when the slit is narrow (a small fraction of a millimetre) the patch of light ab is much wider than the anticipated cd.

Only a wave motion can spread in this way.

Interference Fringes in Young's Double Slit

Allow the light from a bright, narrow source of light S to fall on a double slit, the slits being very narrow and very close together. If a

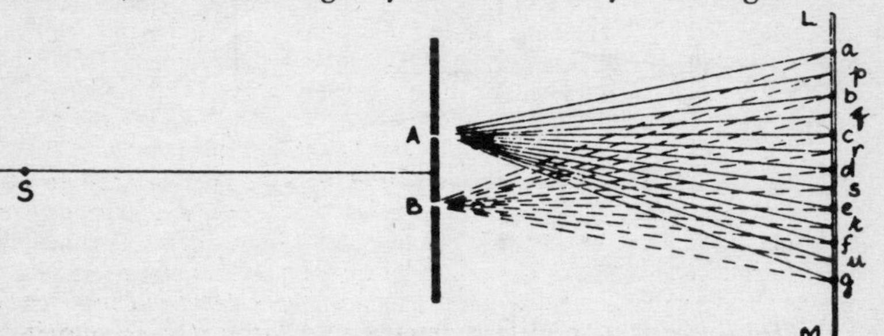

screen LM is allowed to catch the light after it has passed through the slits A and B, a series of alternate bright and dark lines will be seen. These are interference fringes.

At points such as p, q, r, s, t, u the light from the two slits arrives in phase and a bright line appears. At a, b, c, d, e, f, g the light from the two slits arrives a half period out of phase and the two disturbances cancel each other. This produces the series of dark lines.

Unit 3 HEAT

Since energy is the ability to do work then heat is a form of energy because it can be utilized to do work, e.g., the steam engine and internal combustion engine. All forms of energy can be transformed to heat energy efficiently, the reverse is not always true. The temperature of a substance is a measure of its molecular activity (Kinetic theory of matter). The heat content of a substance depends on its temperature, its mass and its heat capacity.

The Transfer of Heat

Heat transfer through a body or between bodies can take place by means of (a) Conduction

(b) Convection

(c) Radiation

Heat *conduction* in solids is a matter of one vibrating molecule nudging its neighbour, thus the vibratory motion is transmitted from one atom to another. The process is identical to sound transmission in a solid but the frequencies of the thermal motions of the atoms are far above our audible range. Heat is also transported in solids by free electrons, it therefore follows that good electrical conductors are good heat conductors. In fact, the heat conductivities of all metals are proportional to their electrical conductivities. Thus poor electrical conductors (e.g. glass, rubber) are also poor heat conductors (insulators). Free electrons move more freely in pure metals than in impure metals (alloys). Some pure metals (and alloys) are better conductors than others.

Convection is more important in gases and liquids. Heat transfer is a result of the differences in densities between cool and heated portions. A heated portion is less dense, (more vigorous molecular activity causes expansion), it rises and allows the cooler portion to take its place until it becomes warm. Convection is decreased by porous materials such as cork, spun glass, rock wool (insulators) which provide many tiny pockets of trapped air to prevent convection.

Radiation is the means by which the sun's heat energy reaches us. Warm objects – in fact all objects whose temperatures are above zero, (0° K or – 27 3° C)– give off radiant energy; the higher the temperature the greater the radiation. Radiant energy is converted to heat only when it is intercepted by a body; it has most of the properties of light waves. The greatest portion of radiant heat comes from the infra-red band just outside the red of the visible spectrum.

Experiment – to show that a dull surface is a better absorber of radiant heat than a polished surface.

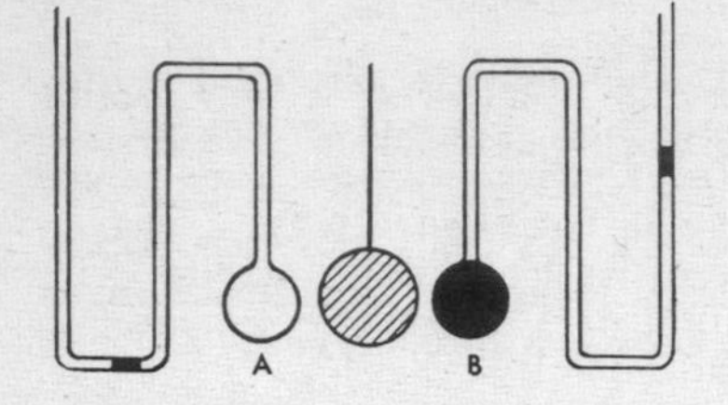

A and B are similar glass bulbs, A is blackened, B is shiny. An electric light bulb is supported symetrically between them. The liquid level rises on the B side. Why?

Experiment – to show that a dull dark surface is a better radiator of heat, than a bright light surface.

The cylinder contains very hot water. Each surface is different. When the cylinder is placed symetrically between the blackened bulbs, so that a dull black surface faces A, and a bright light surface faces B, the liquid moves towards B.

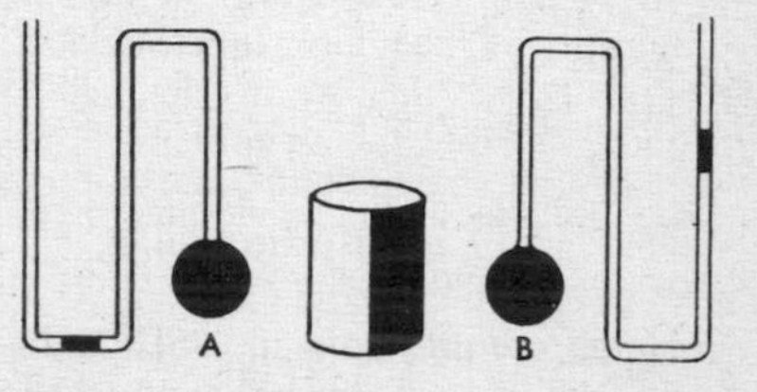

Some materials such as glass will transmit shorter wave lengths of radiant energy than others; rock salt transmits nearly all that strike it. Short wave lengths from the sun will pass through the glass of a greenhouse and heat the soil within. The heated soil gives off longer wave lengths of radiation which the glass will not transmit, thus the greenhouse "traps" heat from the sun.

The Thermos Bottle

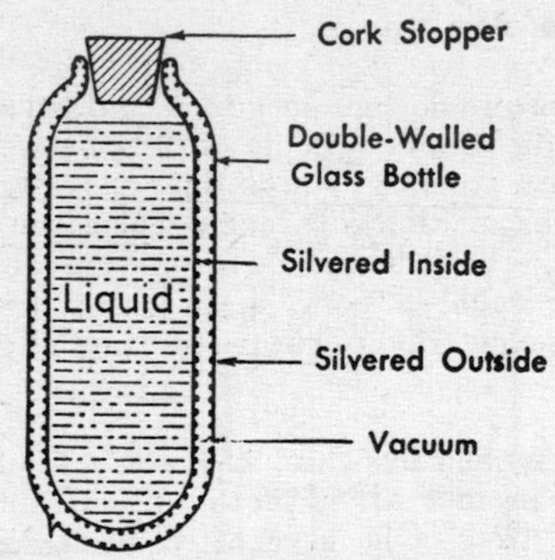

Expansion results when a substance is heated because the greater molecular motion (kinetic energy) forces the molecules further apart. The exception to the rule is water which contracts as it is cooled to 4°C but then begins to expand with further cooling until at 0°C

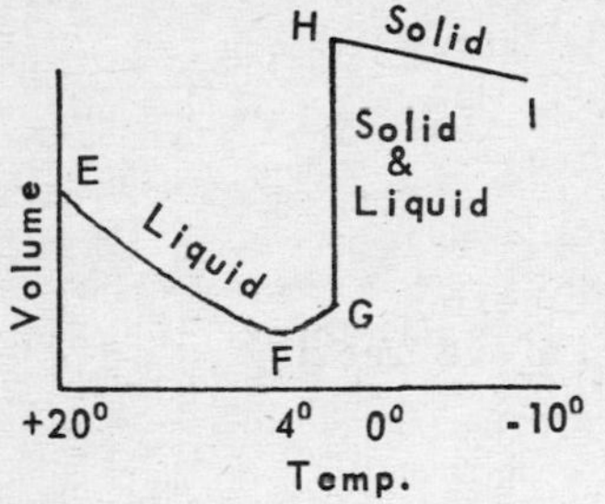

it can exist as a solid or a liquid. The solid (ice) takes on a much greater volume than the liquid at the same temperature, but once it is a solid, further cooling results in contraction. The reason for water's peculiar behaviour lies in its crystaline structure which undergoes complex changes during temperature changes.

Experiments in the expansion of solids, liquids and gases, the unequal expansion of solids (bimetallic strip, thermostat) should be reviewed.

Thermometry

The two common temperature scales are the Fahrenheit and the Centigrade or Celsius. The Fahrenheit scale is used more commonly in homes and industry while the Centigrade is used in science.

The freezing temperature and boiling temperature of pure water are used as starting points in marking the scales on the thermometers.

The Centigrade scale is then divided into 100 equal divisions between 0° and 100° and the Fahrenheit scale is divided into 180 equal divisions between 32° and 212°.

373° K. 100° C. Upper Fixed Point 212°F.
100 divs. C. = 180 divs. F.
1 div. K. = 1 div. C.
∴ 1 div. C. = 9/5 div. F.
273° K. 0° C. 32°F.
Lower Fixed Point
0° K. -273° C. -523.4°F
Kelvin Scale
Celsius Scale
Fahrenheit Scale

Comparing the size of the graduations on each scale it is seen that:

1 F degree = 5/9 C degree
or
1 C degree = 9/5 F degree

Conversion from one scale to the other:

Example 1.

Change a reading of 20°C to a Fahrenheit reading.

Solution:

20°C = 9/5 × 20 or 36 F degrees above freezing

$\therefore$ 20°C = (36 + 32)°F = 68°F

Formula: $F = 9/5C + 32$.

Example 2:

Change 77°F to a Centigrade reading.

Solution:

77°F is (77−32) or 45F degrees above freezing
45F degrees = 5/9 x 45 = 25C degrees above freezing

∴ 77°F = 25°C

Formula: C = 5/9 x (F−32)

The Kelvin (Absolute) Scale

A third temperature scale called the Kelvin or Absolute scale is used in science. The Kelvin degree is the same size as the Centigrade degree but the boiling point of water on the K scale is 373°K and the ice point is 273°K. This scale also uses what is called Kelvin's absolute zero, which is equivalent to − 273°C. At this temperature it is believed that all molecular motion stops.

Centigrade readings may be converted to K readings by using the formula:

°K = °C + 273

Quantity of Heat

Temperature and quantity of heat should not be confused. One gram of water and one Kgm of water in separate containers can be at the *same temperature* but certainly the larger contains the greater quantity of heat and required the greater quantity of heat to warm it through the same temperature range. The same mass of alcohol would require less heat to get it to the same temperature.

The quantity of heat in a substance depends on three important factors:

(a) its temperature

(b) its mass

(c) the nature of the substance, i.e. its heat capacity.

Heat Capacity – Specific Heat

The units of heat are the Calorie in the metric system and the British Thermal Unit (B.T.U.) in the English system.

The calorie is defined as the quantity of heat required to raise the temperature of one gram of water through 1 centigrade degree.

The B.T.U. is defined as the heat required to raise the temperature of one lb. of water through one Fahrenheit degree.

The B.T.U. is the larger heat unit,

1 BTU = 252 calories.

Example Problems:

1. What heat is gained when 1 kg of water is heated from 10°C to 80°C?

Solution 1:

Heat gained when:
1 gm of water is warmed 1C° = 1 cal.
1000 gm of water are warmed 1C° = 1000 x 1 = 1000 cal.
1000 gm of water are warmed (80 – 10)C° = 1000 x 70 x 1
= 70,000 cal.

Solution 2:

Heat gained = mass water x temp. change x 1
= 1000 x (80 – 10) x 1
= 70,000 cal.

2. What heat is lost by 1 ton of water cooling from 60 to 50°F?

Solution:

Heat lost when:
1 lb. of water cools 1F° = 1 B.T.U.
2000 lb. of water cools 1F° = 2000 x 1 = 2000 cal.
2000 lb. of water cools (60 – 50)F° = 2000 x 10 x 1
= 20,000 B.T.U.

or

Heat lost = mass x temp. change x 1
= 2000 x (60 – 50) x 1
= 20,000 B.T.U.

HEAT CAPACITY

By comparing the heat lost by a given mass of water with the heat lost by an equal mass of some other substance when cooling through the same temperature range, we can obtain a good idea of the relative heat capacities of various materials.

Experiment to compare the heat capacities of lead and alcohol with that of water.

Put 100 gm of water at room temperature into each of three beakers. Record the temperature of each.

Heat 100 gm of alcohol and 100 gm of water in separate beakers, to 75°C. Heat 100 gm of lead shot to the same temperature by placing it in a small metal container in a beaker of boiling water; agitate the lead with the thermometer while watching its temperature.

As each reaches 75°C pour it quickly into a beaker containing the 100 gm of water at room temperature. Stir with a thermometer and read the final temperature of the mixtures. The final temperature will be approximately as shown in the diagram below.

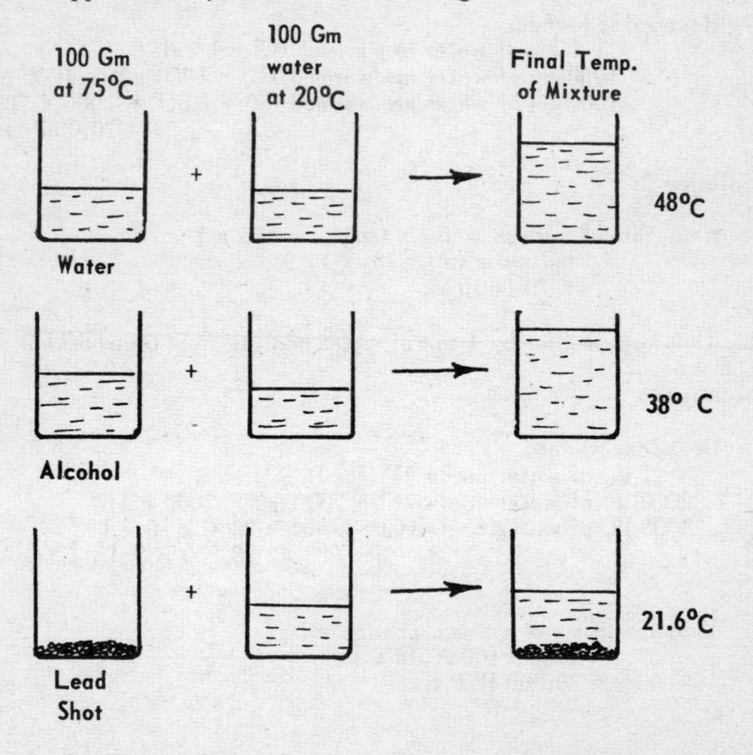

In each case heat was lost by the warm material to the 100 gm of water at room temperature. Obviously the 100 gm of warm water contained the greatest quantity of heat, alcohol was next and the lead contained the least.

In other words heat capacities of materials vary. Water has the highest heat capacity of all common materials.

The heat required to raise the temperature of 1 gm of water 1C° is by definition, 1 calorie. By such experiments as above it could be shown that the heat required to raise the temperature of 1 gm of alcohol 1C° would be about 0.55 calories, and lead 0.03 calories. In other words the heat capacity of alcohol is about 55% of that of water and lead about 3%.

These values, 0.55 for alcohol, 0.03 for lead and 1 for water are called the *specific heats* of the materials.

Specific heat is defined as the heat required to raise the temperature of one gm of any substance through 1 centigrade degree. In the English system it is the heat required to raise the temperature of 1 lb. of a substance 1F°.

Example Problems:

1. Determine the specific heat of the alcohol in the last experiment. Use the same type of solution as for lead.

2. How much heat is required to raise the temperature of 50 gm of mercury from 20°C to 60°C? (S.H. of mercury = 0.033.)

Solution:

Heat required = mass x temp. change x S.H.
= 50 x 40 x 0.033
= 66 cal.

3. How much heat is lost when 10 lb. of lead cools from 150°F to 80°F?

Solution:

Temperature change = 150–80 = 70F°.
Heat lost = mass x temp. change x S.H.
= 10 x 70 x 0.03 = 21 B.T.U.

Note: The S.H. of lead being 0.03 means that 0.03 cal. will raise the temp. of 1 gm of lead 1C° *or* that 0.03 B.T.U. will raise the temp.

of 1 lb. of lead 1F°. In other words the numbers given for specific heats of materials can be used in either the metric or English systems.

Heat involved in Changes of State

Put some ice in a beaker over a gentle flame. Stir vigorously with a thermometer and note the temperature as the ice melts.

The ice-water mixture will remain at 0°C as long as ice is present despite the fact that heat is being added.

Similarly the temperature of boiling water will remain at about 100°C (depending on altitude) as long as water is present, again despite the fact that heat is being added.

In each case heat is being absorbed without a change in temperature. The heat (energy) is required to change the state of the material and a change in state involves simply a change in molecular activity of the material. Heat is always required to set the molecules of a substance in a state of more vigorous motion and of course, more vigorous motion results if heat is added. Water molecules are more active than ice molecules so heat is required to melt the ice. Vapor molecules are more vigorously in motion than water molecules thus heat is required to change water to water vapor.

Heat of Fusion

Every gram of ice requires a definite quantity of heat to change it to water. Also, every gram of water gives off the same quantity of heat when it freezes.

The heat of fusion of ice is defined as the quantity of heat required to change one gram of ice at 0°C to water at 0°C.

Experiment: To determine the heat of fusion of ice.

Weigh an empty glass tumbler. Put 200 gm (200 cc) of water at about 25°C into the tumbler and record the water temperature. Estimate about 25 cc of melting ice and add it to the water after drying as well as possible with a paper towel. Stir well with a thermometer and just as the last piece of ice disappears record the temperature. Now weigh the tumbler and contents in order to find the weight of ice used. The following recordings of such an experiment are typical:

Weight of empty tumbler	300 gm
Temp. of warm water	25°C
Weight of warm water	200 gm
Wt. of tumbler, water and melted ice	520 gm
Weight of ice	20 gm

Final temp. of mixture	15°C
Specific heat of water	1
Let heat of fusion of ice be	x

The ice will absorb heat from the warm water to change its state without a change in temperature. That is, the ice at 0°C will absorb heat while it changed to water at 0°C. Also the resulting water at 0°C (ice water) will absorb additional heat to bring its final temperature to 15°C.

Heat required to melt ice + heat required to warm ice water
= heat lost by warm water

or

H. of F x Mass Ice + (Mass x Temp. change x S.H) ice water
= (Mass x temp. change x S.H) warm water

$$\therefore x20 + 20 \times (15-0) \times 1 = 200 \times (25-15) \times 1$$
$$20x + 300 = 5000 - 3000$$
$$x = 1700 \div 20 = 85$$

$\therefore$ S.H. of ice is 85 calories per gram.

Note (1): The accepted value is 80 cal. per gram.

Note (2): In the calculations in this experiment the heat capacity of the container has not been considered.

Example Problem

1. How much heat is absorbed by 1 kgm of ice at 0°C when it changes to water at 10°C?

Solution 1.

Heat required to change:
1 gm of ice at 0°C to water at 0°C = 80 cal.
1000 gm of ice at 0°C to water at 0°C = 80 x 1000
= 80,000 cal.

Heat required to warm:
1 gm of water 1C° = 1 cal.
1000 gm of water 1C° = 1000 x 1 cal.
1000 gm of water 10C° = 1000 x 10 x 1

$\therefore$ Total heat required = 80,000 + 10,000 = 90,000 cal.

Solution 2.

Total heat absorbed
= (H of F x Mass) ice + (Mass x Temp. chge x S.H.) ice water
= 80 x 1000 + 1000 x 10 x 1
= 90,000 cal.

Heat of Vaporization

Every gram of water at 100°C requires a definite quantity of heat to change its state to steam without a change of temperature. This heat is called the heat of vaporization.

The heat of vaporization of water is defined as the heat required to change 1 gm of water at 100°C to steam at 100°C:

The accepted value of the H. of V. of water is 540 cal. per gram.

It should be noted that when steam at 100°C condenses to water at 100°C the same 540 cal. of heat are released. Thus steam is an excellent means of heating buildings. When it condenses in the radiators large quantities of heat are released.

Example Problems

1. What heat is required to change 1 kgm of water at 100°C to steam at 100°C?

Solution

Heat required to change:
1 gm of water at 100°C to steam at 100°C = 540 cal.
1000 gm of water at 100°C to steam at 100°C = 540 x 1000
= 540,000 cal.

2. What heat is required to change 10 gm of ice at 0°C to steam at 100°C?

Solution

Total heat required
= (H of F x Mass) ice + (Mass x Temp. chge. x S.H) water
+ (H of V x Mass)
= (80 x 10) + (10 x 100 x 1) + (540 x 10) = 7200 cal.

The Calorimeter

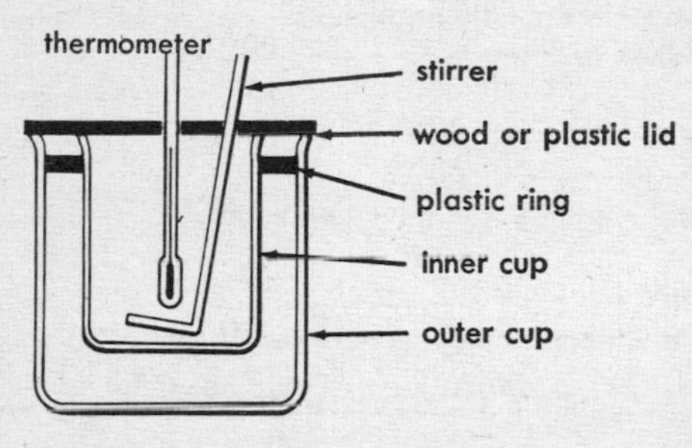

In the foregoing experiments the heat capacities of the containers were not considered. This would introduce some error because the container will take on the same temperature as its contents and will therefore absorb heat from the contents when warming and give heat to the contents when cooling. The heat given off or absorbed by the container will depend on its mass, temperature change and specific heat. To further increase the accuracy of such experiments the heat loss or gain to the surroundings is minimized by proper design of the calorimeter. Can you explain how each component does this?

Heat of Vaporization of Water

An experiment to determine the H. of V. of water using the calorimeter and other apparatus shown in the diagram would yield the typical observations shown below. The steam (at 100°C) will condense in the cool water of the calorimeter giving off its heat of vaporization.

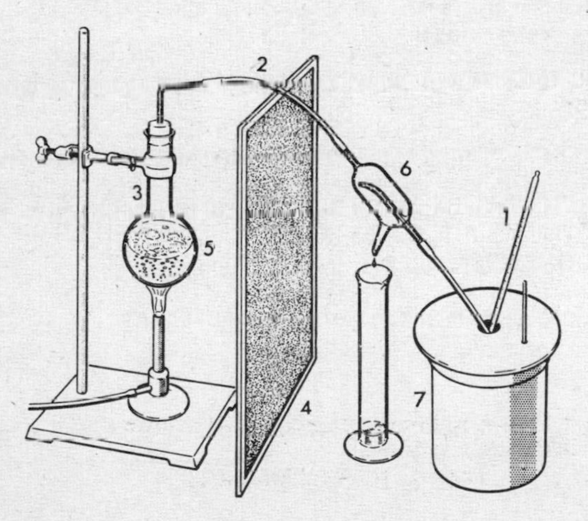

1. – Thermometer
2. – Glass tubing
3. – Steam generator
4. – Heat shield
5. – Boiling water
6. – Condensed water trap
7. – Colorimeter

Observations:

Mass of inner vessel - 40 gm
Mass of inner vessel and water - - - - - - 332 gm
$\therefore$ Mass of cool water - 292 gm

Initial temp. of water - - - - - - - - - - - - - $20^{\circ}C$
Final temp. of water mixture - - - - - - - - $40^{\circ}C$
$\therefore$ Temp. change of cool water - - - - - - - - - - - - - - - $20C^{\circ}$

Mass of inner vessel and mixture - - - - - 392 gm
$\therefore$ Mass of steam condensed - - - - - - - - - - - - - - - - - 10 gm

Specific Heat of vessel - 0.20

Let H. of V. of water be x cal/gm.

Calculations:

The condensing steam gives off H. of V. to warm the cool water and calorimeter; the condensate formed (at $100^{\circ}C$) will cool down to the final mixture temperature warming the cool water and calorimeter further.

(M x H of V) steam + (M x Tch x SH) condensate
= (M x Tch x SH) water + (M x Tch x SH) cal.

$$10x + 10 \times (100 - 40) \times 1 = 292 \times (40 - 20) \times 1 + 40 \times (40 - 20) \times .2$$
$$10x + 600 = 5840 + 160$$
$$x = 540$$

$\therefore$ H. of V of steam = 540 cal/gm.

Example Problem

A calorimeter weighing 100 gm contains an ice-water mixture of 120 gm ice and 80 gm water. What mass of steam at $100^{\circ}C$ will bring the temp. of the mixture to $50^{\circ}C$?

(S. H. cal = 0.20; H of F ice = 80; H of V of water = 540)

Solution:

Let mass of steam be x gm

Heat gained by:

(i) Calorimeter = M x Tch x SH = 100 x (50 – 0) x 0.20 = 1000 cal.

(ii) Water = M x Tch x SH = 80 x (50 – 0) x 1 = 4000 cal.

(iii) ice at 0^0 changing
to water at 0^oC = H of F x M = 80 x 120 = 9600 cal.

(iv) water formed by ice = M x Tch x SH = 120 x 50 x 1 = 6000 cal.

Total heat gained = 20,600 cal.

Heat lost by:

(i) steam condensing = H of V x M = 540 × x = 540x cal.

(ii) condensate at 100^oC
cooling to final temp. = M x Tch x Sh = x × (100–50)x1 = 50x cal.

Total heat lost = 590x cal.

Heat lost = Heat gained

∴ 590x = 20,600

x = 34.9

∴ Mass of steam required = 35 gm

Unit 4 ELECTRICITY

The Source of Electricity

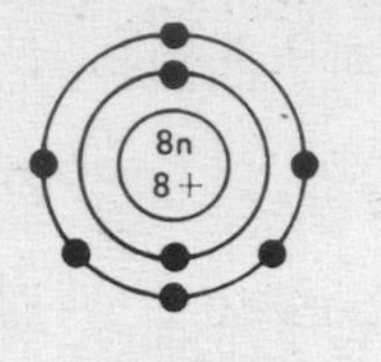

Electrons (•), Protons (+), Neutrons (n)

All atoms are made up of a central group of particles called the nucleus and tiny particles called electrons which "orbit" the nucleus. The electron is always a negatively charged particle. For each electron in a neutral atom there is a positive particle called a proton in the nucleus. Some atoms have many electrons orbiting the nucleus (Uranium has 92). If an electron can be removed from an atom it becomes a "free electron". The atom is then left with a deficiency of electrons and is therefore a positively charged particle (an ion). Sometimes atoms gain extra electrons in which case they are negatively charged particles or ions.

The motion or accumulation of electrons is in fact our source of electricity.

Static electricity is created by friction between objects and the objects are said to be "charged" with static electricity. Most people have experienced a spark from their finger tips when touching a metal object after walking across a rug. Clouds build up static charged by friction of the air during turbulence, and the discharge is seen as lightning.

For laboratory work known charges can be produced by rubbing ebonite with cat's fur, and glass with silk. The ebonite becomes negatively charged and the glass positively charged.

The Laws of Behaviour of Static Charges

When a charged ebonite rod (negative) is suspended by a string and approached by a second charged ebonite rod, a repelling force becomes apparent between the two rods. If a charged glass rod is brought near the suspended ebonite rod a definite attracting force will be apparent. Similarly two charged glass rods (+) will repel each other. Thus the laws of electrostatics: like charges repel, unlike charges attract.

Charging By Contact

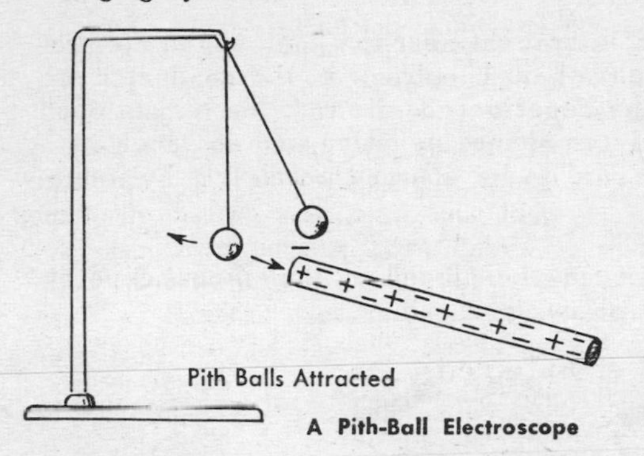

A Pith-Ball Electroscope

An electroscope is an instrument used to detect the presence of, and identify, static charges.

If the pith-ball is touched by a charged ebonite rod it will be seen first to be attracted then will be repelled indicating that the pith-ball has become negatively charged by contact with the ebonite rod. Electrons are actually transferred to the ball during contact giving it a surplus and therefore a negative charge.

Induced Static Charges

If a negatively charged pith-ball is suspended near but not touching the end of a metal conductor and a charged ebonite rod is brought near the other end of the conductor, the ball will be noticeably repelled. A charge has been induced in the conductor by the nearness of the ebonite rod. If a charged glass rod is used, the ball will be attracted indicating that the conductor has been charged positively by induction. When the rods are removed the conductor is no longer charged – it was charged temporarily by induction. The ebonite rod repelled free electrons in the conductor causing a surplus and therefore a negative charge at the far end.

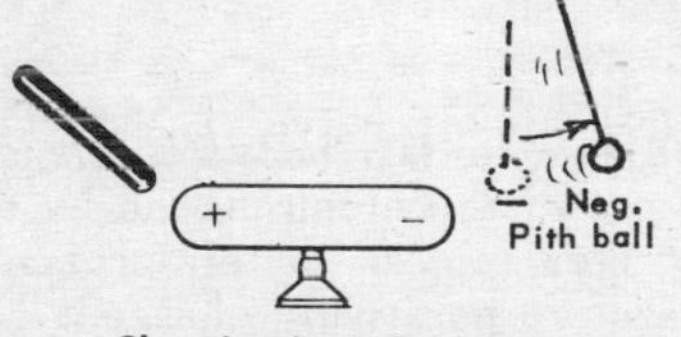

Charging by induction

The Metal Leaf Electroscope

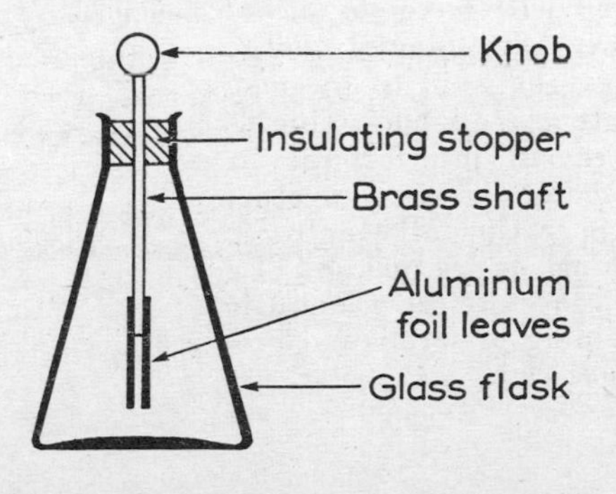

Charging the Metal Leaf Electroscope by Induction

When a charged ebonite rod is brought near the knob of the electroscope the leaves repel each other. Electrons in the conductor are repelled to the leaves by the negative ebonite rod, the leaves each now having a surplus of electrons are negative and so repel each other. The electroscope is said to be charged negatively by induction.

A permanent induced charge may be placed on the electroscope by the sequence shown in the following drawings.

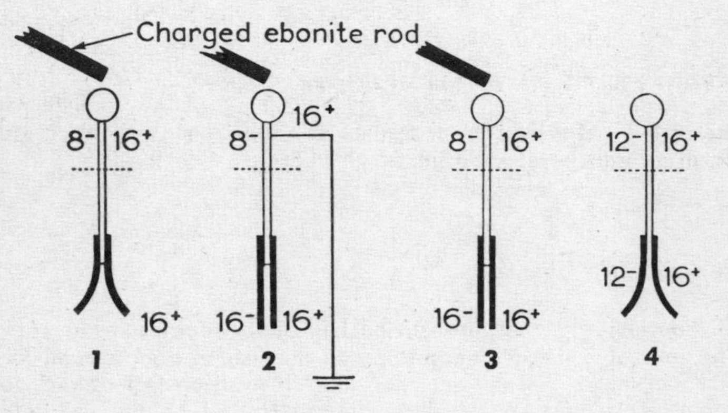

By touching the knob we are "grounding" it. Our body readily absorbs the electrons that are repelled out of the electroscope by the ebonite rod. Removing the "ground" then leaves the electroscope with a deficiency of electrons and therefore positively charged. The earth is a much more efficient ground than our bodies.

Shielding

If a piece of metal screen is shaped so as to surround but not touch the knob of the electroscope and then grounded, the charged ebonite rod will have no effect on the electroscope. Any induced charge is grounded and may be said to by-pass the electroscope into ground. Such shielding is used to prevent interference by static charges in the atmosphere or other sources with the operation of electronic equipment. Shielding on radio and TV tubes is usually in the form of a metallic coating. The shielding absorbs and grounds static charges.

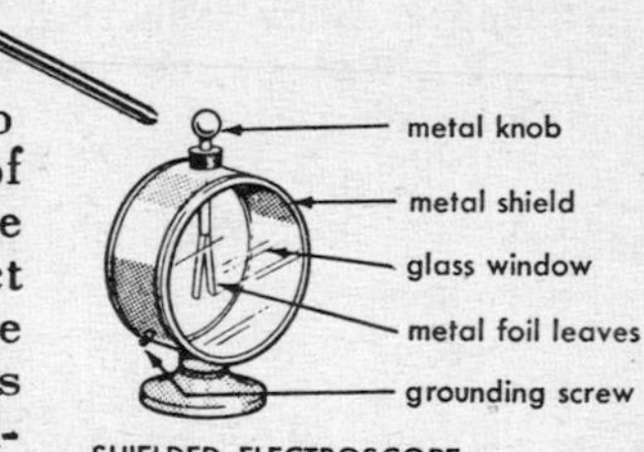

SHIELDED ELECTROSCOPE

Conductors and Insulators

A good electrical conductor is made up of atoms whose electrons can be easily removed from their orbits. The electrons flow through the conductor and create or carry an electric current. Metals, acid and alkali solutions are good conductors.

When materials have atoms whose electrons are not easily removed they are usually good insulators. Rubber, pure water, mica, glass, plastic and many others are such materials.

Current Electricity

The discharge of the static (Wimshurst) machine and lightning are visible evidence of the motion of electrons which in fact is current electricity.

Many forms of energy can be transformed to electrical energy. The generator transforms rotary mechanical energy to electricity through electromagnetic induction. Chemical energy in storage cells is converted to electrical energy when the terminals are connected to a "load". Radiant energy is converted to electrical energy in the solar (sun) battery.

Some Electrical Symbols

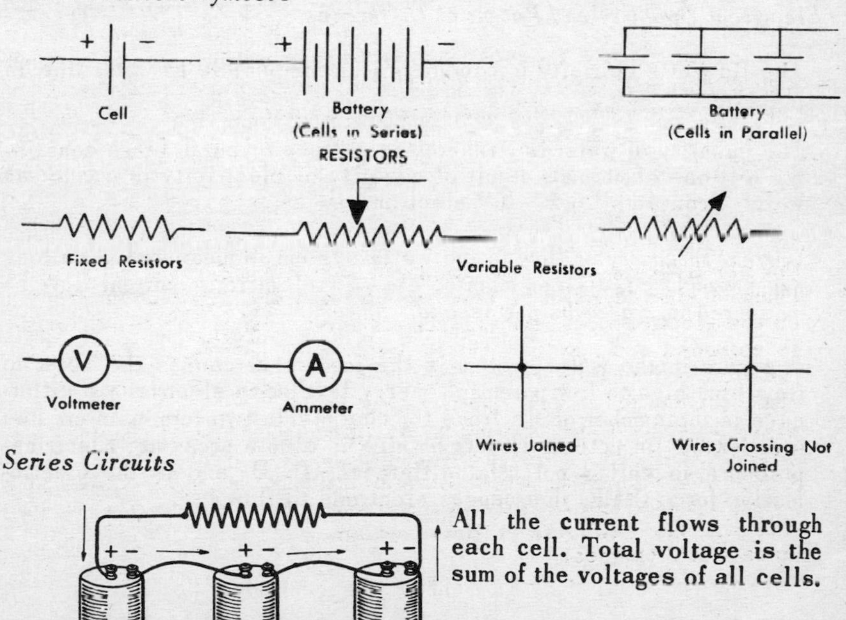

Series Circuits

All the current flows through each cell. Total voltage is the sum of the voltages of all cells.

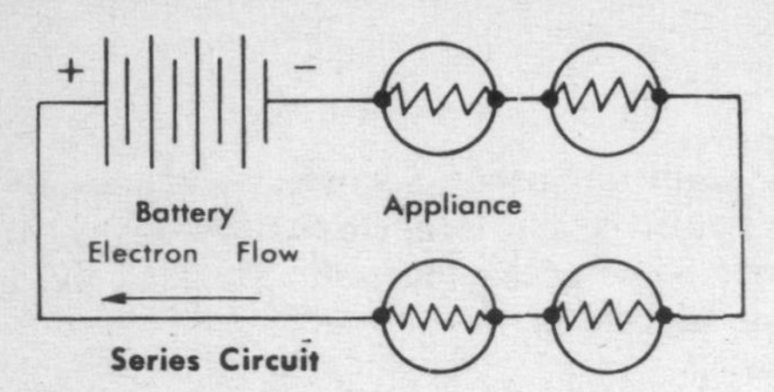

If any appliance is disconnected or burned out, all go out. Same current flows through all cells and appliances.

Parallel Circuits

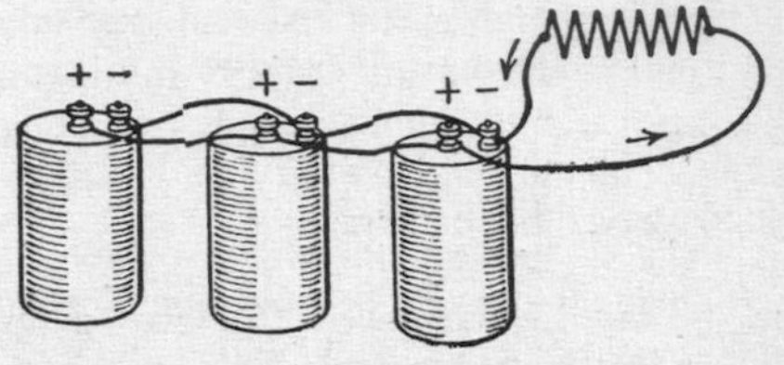

When cells are connected in parallel, the voltage is the same as the voltage of a single cell. All the positive terminals are connected by one wire and all the negative terminals by the other wire.

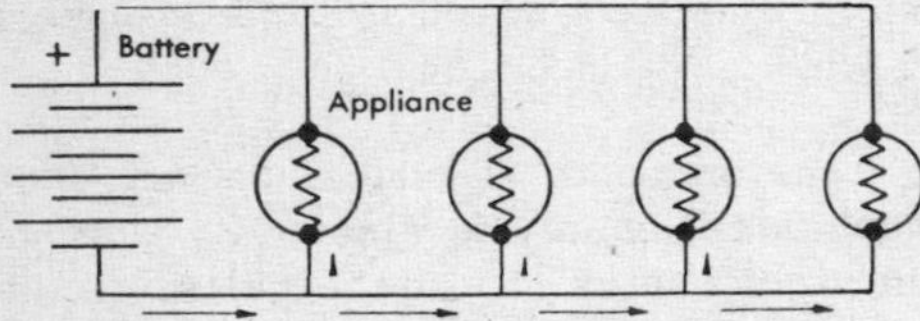

Appliances and Cells in Parallel

Each cell and appliance operates independently of the others.

Electrical Quantity and Potential Difference

The flow of electricity in conductors is comparable to water flow in pipes.

The *quantity* of water is measured in gallons or cu. ft. (each containing billions of atoms); a unit of quantity of electricity is a *coulomb* which "contains" 6.2×10^{18} electrons.

Current intensity or flow in the water system is measured in gallons per second, cu. ft. per minute, etc.; in electricity current flow is measured in *coulombs* per *second.*

Pressure in the water system is the force that causes the water to flow from high to low potential energy levels; in electricity a difference in the number of electrons (or charges) in two terminals creates a difference in potential energy which is also a pressure. Electrical pressure is called potential difference (P. D) and is the electromotive force (EMF) that causes electrons to flow.

Electrical Units

Quantity (Q) is measured in coulombs.

Current Intensity (I) is measured in coulombs per second, one coulomb per second is *defined* as *one ampere.*

Potential Difference (P. D) is measured in *volts* (V). One volt is defined as the P. D. between two points when it takes 1 Joule of work to move 1 coulomb from one of the points to the other.

The Electrical Equivalent of Heat

Electricity can be converted to heat in conductors, (e.g. toasters, stoves, etc.). Work must be done to move the electrons whose K.E. is in turn converted to heat. The work done must correspond to the heat produced.

We have defined one volt of P.D. as equivalent to one joule per coulomb: $1 \text{ volt (V)} = \dfrac{1 \text{ joule (W)}}{1 \text{ coulamb (Q)}}$

$$\therefore V = \frac{W}{Q} \text{ or } W = VQ \text{ - - - - - -1.}$$

Also 1 ampere (I) is defined as 1 coulomb (Q) per sec. (t)

$$\therefore I = \frac{Q}{t} \text{ or } Q = I\,t \text{ - - - - - - 2.}$$

Substituting Q from 2 into equation 1 :

$$W = V\,I\,t \text{ (joules = volts} \times \text{amps.} \times \text{sec.)}$$

The work equivalent of the current in a circuit can be calculated if values of V, I and t are known.

The following apparatus plus a stop watch will allow us to calculate the electrical equivalent of heat.

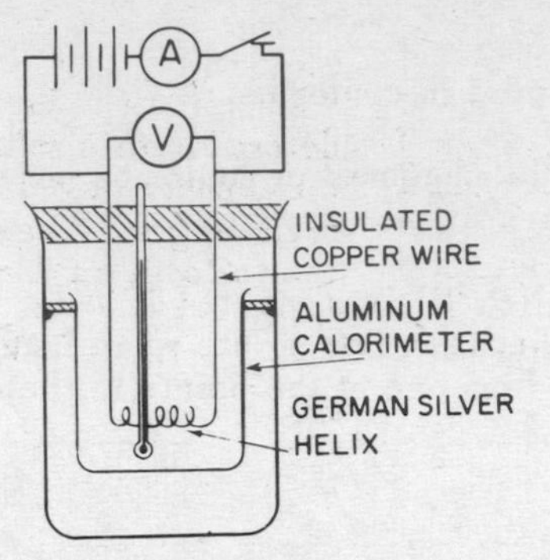

The following readings are typical:

Mass of inner vessel	40 gms
Mass of inner vessel and water	190 gms
Initial temp. of water	15° C
Final temp. of water	35° C
Current (I)	4.0 amps.
P. D. (V)	11 volts
Time (t) (5 min.)	300 secs.
Mass of water (190 – 40) =	150 gms
Temp. chge. water (35 – 15) =	20 C°
S. H. calorimeter =	0.20

Calculations :

Heat gained by cal. and water = $40 \times 20 \times 0.20 + 150 \times 20 \times 1$
= 160 + 3000
= 3160 cals.

Electrical work done, W = V I t
= $11 \times 4 \times 300$
= 13200 joules

$\therefore$ 3160 cals. of heat were produced by 13200 joules of electrical energy.

$\therefore$ 1 cal. is equivalent to $\frac{13200}{3160}$ = 4.18 joules

The electrical equivalent of heat is given the symbol J. Its equivalent in electrical work units (W) per unit of heat (H) has been found by experiment and may be written: $J = \frac{W \text{ (joules)}}{H \text{ (cals.)}}$ = 4.18 joules/col.

Note: The accepted value for J is 4.18 joules/col.

Ohm's Law – Relation Between V and I

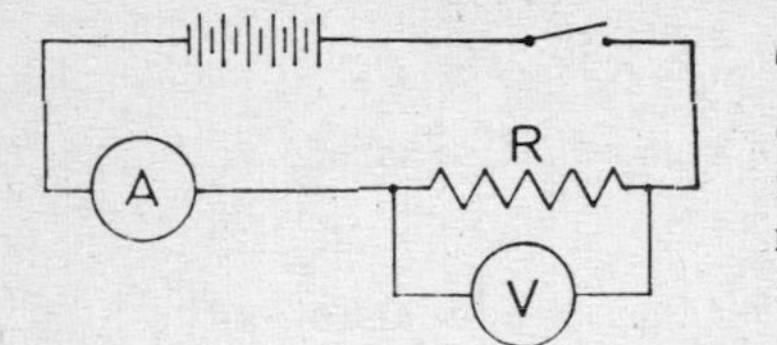

The circuit shown can be used to determine this relationship by varying the number of cells in the circuit and recording readings as represented in the following table.

No. of Cells	V (volts)	I (amps)	$\frac{V}{I}$
1	1.5	0.3	5
2	3.0	0.6	5
3	4.5	0.9	5
4	6.0	1.2	5

Thus $\frac{V}{I}$ is a constant and this is true for any conductor. This constant is called the *resistance* of the conductor, it is given the symbol (R) and it is measured in *ohms*. $\therefore \frac{V}{I} = R$ or $V = I R$

Note also that when the voltage is doubled the current is doubled; when V is tripled, I is tripled. In other words V is proportional to I.

Ohm's Law: the current through a conductor is proportional to the P.D. between its ends.

One ohm of resistance is defined as the resistance which will allow a current of one ampere to flow through the conductor when the P.D. between the end of the conductor is one volt.

Factors Affecting the Resistance of a Conductor

(1) The kind of material (no. of free electrons)

(2) The longer it is the higher its resistance

(3) The greater its diameter the lower its resistance

(4) The higher the temp. of the conductor the higher its resistance

R and V in Series Circuits

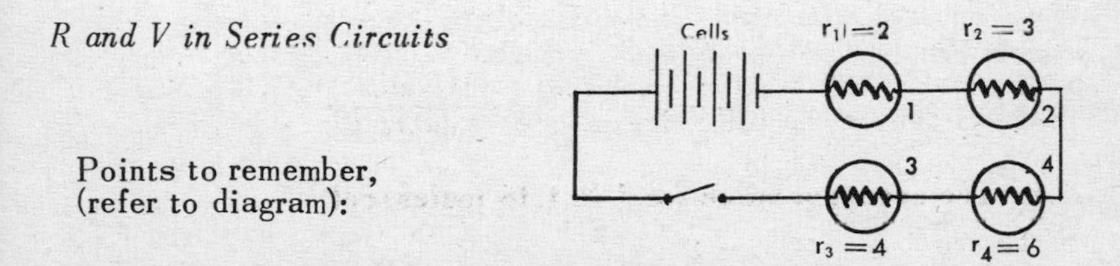

Points to remember,
(refer to diagram):

(1) Total R in series is the *sum* of separate resistances
Eg. $R = r_1 + r_2 + r_3 + r_4 = 2 + 3 + 4 + 6 = 15$ ohms

(2) Total P.D. of cells in series is the sum of all separate voltages
Eg. $V = 4 \times 1.5 = 6$ volts

(3) The current is the same through all items and depends on the total V and total R.
Eg. $V = 6.0$ volts, $R = 15$ ohms $\therefore I = \frac{V}{R} = \frac{6}{15} = .4$ amps

(4) The P.D. between the ends of any separate conductor depends on the individual R of the conductor.
Eg. P.D. of item (3), $V_3 = Ir_3 = 0.4 \times 4 = 1.6$ volts

Resistances and Voltages in Parallel

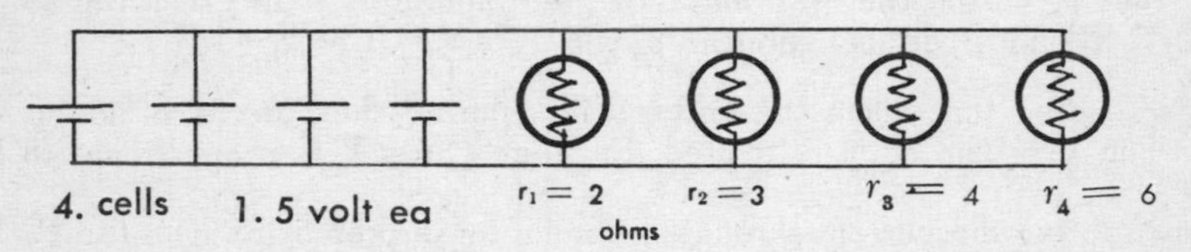

Points to remember :

(1) Total voltage available is the same as that of a single cell
Eg. 1.5 V

(2) The *equivalent* resistance is determined from the formula:
$\frac{1}{R} = \frac{1}{r_1} + \frac{1}{r_2} + \frac{1}{r_3} + \frac{1}{r_4}$
Eg. $\frac{1}{R} = \frac{1}{2} + \frac{1}{3} + \frac{1}{4} + \frac{1}{6} = \frac{5}{4}$
$\therefore \frac{R}{1}$ or $R = \frac{4}{5}$ ohms

(3) The P.D. between the ends of any item is the same as the total available, eg. 1.5 volts.

(4) The current through any item depends on its own resistance
Eg. I of item (1) $= \frac{V}{r_1} = \frac{1.5}{2} = 0.75$ amps

Example Problem

In the circuit on the following page calculate:

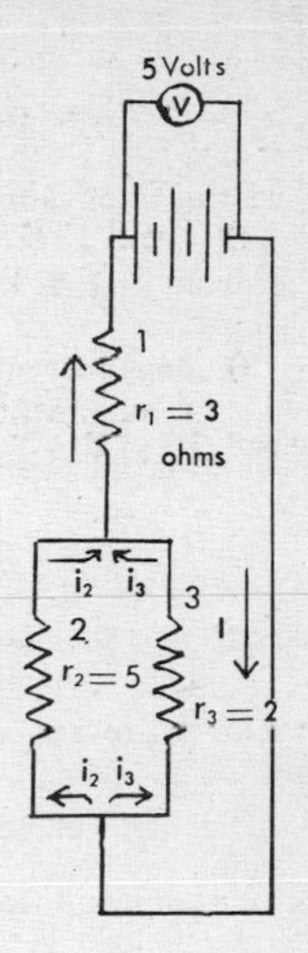

(a) The effective R of the parallel group

(b) Total R of the circuit

(c) I through item (1)

(d) PD across the parallel group

(e) I through item (3)

(f) I through item (2)

Solution :

(a) For the parallel group, $\frac{1}{R} = \frac{1}{r_2} + \frac{1}{r_3} = \frac{1}{5} + \frac{1}{2} = \frac{7}{10}$

$\therefore$ Effective R in parallel = $\frac{10}{7}$ = 1.4 ohms

(b) Total R of circuit = r_1 + effective R in parallel
= 3 + 1.4 = 4.4 ohms

(c) Current through (1) depends on total PD and total R of circuit

$\therefore$ $I = \frac{V}{R} = \frac{5}{4.4}$ = 1.13 amps

(d) First find PD across (1),- $V_1 = I r_1$ = 1.13 × 3 = 3.39 volts

$\therefore$ PD across parallel group = 5 – 3.39 = 1.61 volts

or PD across parallel group is same as PD across its effective R, (1.4 ohms), i.e., $I R_e$ = 1.13 × 1.4 = 1.6 volts

(e) Current in item (3), i_3, depends on its resistance and PD

r_3 = 2 ohms; V_3 = 1·6, $\therefore$ $i_3 = \frac{V_3}{r_3} = \frac{1.6}{2}$ = 0.8 amps

(f) Current I of 1.13 amps is shared by items (2) and (3) as it passes through the parallel group.

i.e. $I = i_2 + i_3$ $\therefore$ $i_2 = I - i_3$

$\therefore$ i_2 = 1.13 – 0.8 = 0.33 amps

Cost of Electrical Energy

It has been shown that $W = V I t$ joules.

Power is the rate of doing work, i.e. work done per unit of time:

$$P(\text{watts}) = \frac{W\ (\text{joules})}{t\ (\text{sec})}$$

Combining these two equations,

$$P\ (\text{watts}) = \frac{V I t}{t} = V I\ (\text{volts x amps})$$

$$P = V I \text{ watts}$$

The following units are useful in power problems

1 KW = 1000 watts

1 horsepower, HP = 746 watts

Electrical appliances are rated according to the energy they consume, eg, light bulbs are rated at 25, 40, 60, 100, etc. watts; an iron might be rated at 750 watts, a radio at 40 watts. When one kw of energy is used for one hour the consumer pays for one kilowatt-hour (kwh) of energy.

kwh's = power (kw) x time (hrs)

Example Problems

1. What power in Kw is required to run an electric motor which uses 7 amps at PD of 110 volts?

   How much will it cost to run the motor for 10 hours at 4 cents per Kw hr?

Solution: $P = V \times I = 110 \times 7 = 770$ watts

$$= \frac{770}{1000} = 0.77 \text{ Kw}$$

No. of Kw hr. = 0.77 x 10 = 7.7 Kw hr.
Cost at 4¢ = 7.7 x 4 = 30.8 cents

2. What voltage is required by a 1.1 Kw heater which draws 10 amps? What is the cost of operating it for 14 hours at 3 cents per Kw hr?

Solution: 1·1 Kw = 1100 watts

$P = VI$ watts

or $V = \frac{P}{I} = \frac{1100}{10} = 110$ volts

No. of Kw hrs. consumed = 1.1 x 24 = 26.4

$\therefore$ Cost of 24 hrs. at 3¢ = 26.4 x 3 = 79¢

4. How much does it cost to cook a turkey for 6 hours in an oven that uses 10 amps. at 220 volts, if the cost of 1 Kw hr. of energy is 3¢?

Solution: Power = V x I = 220 x 10 = 2200 watts
= 2·2 Kw
Energy consumed = 2.2 x 6 = 13.2 Kw hr.

$\therefore$ Cost of cooking turkey = 3 x 13.2 = 40¢

Electromagnetism

Magnetic substances are those that are attracted by a magnet; nickel, cobalt and iron are the most common; others are non magnetic. Materials that are easily magnetized are said to be *permeable.*

Laws of Magnetism: like poles repel, unlike poles attract.

Magnetic line of force are conventionally said to "flow" from N to S (the direction taken by the N of a compass needle)

The earth is a huge magnet. Notice that the magnetic pole in the Northern Hemisphere actually has south magnetism and the magnetic pole in the Southern Hemisphere has north magnetism. What effect does this have on a compass?

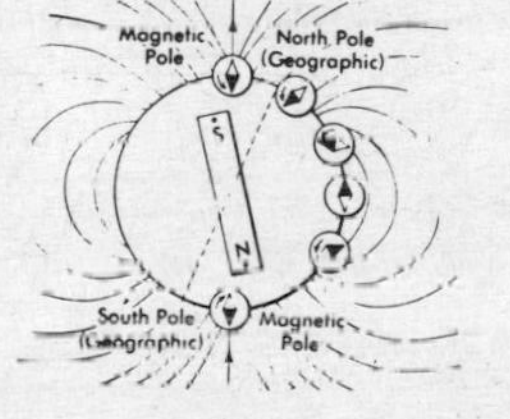

Induced Magnetism occurs in a magnetic substance when it is placed in the field of force of a magnet and disappears when removed. The more permeable a substance is (soft iron) the greater its induced magnetism.

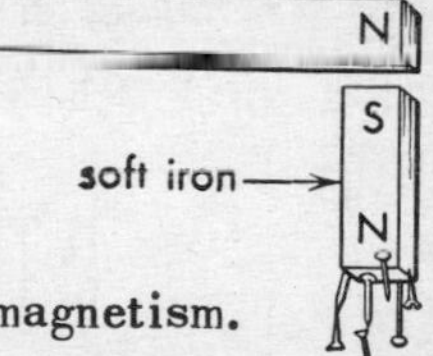

The theory of magnetism states that while unmagnitized, the N and S poles of the "molecular" magnets of a substance are randomly orientated cancelling each others strength.

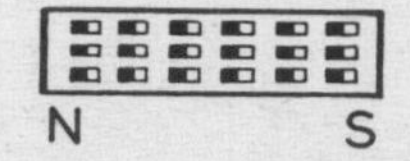

When all the N's of the molecular magnets are lined up in the same direction (as occurs in soft iron by induction) their fields strengthen each other to create a unified magnetic field as in a single bar magnet.

The Magnetic Effect of Electrons in Motion

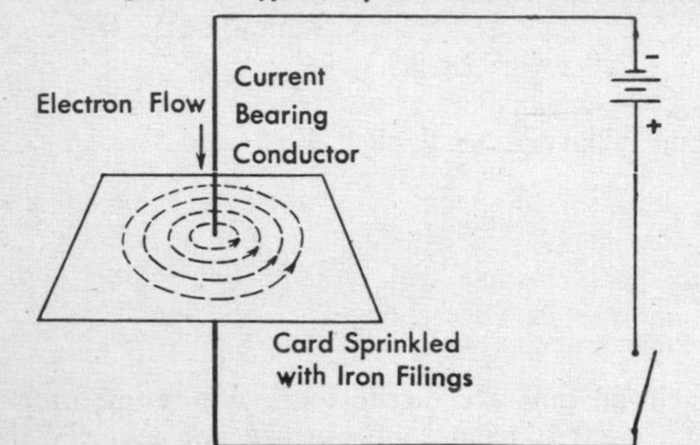

When a conductor is connected to the terminals of a dry cell the presence of a magnetic field can be detected by iron filings and a compass needle. If the terminals are reversed the compass needle is deflected in the opposite direction.

The Left Hand Rule

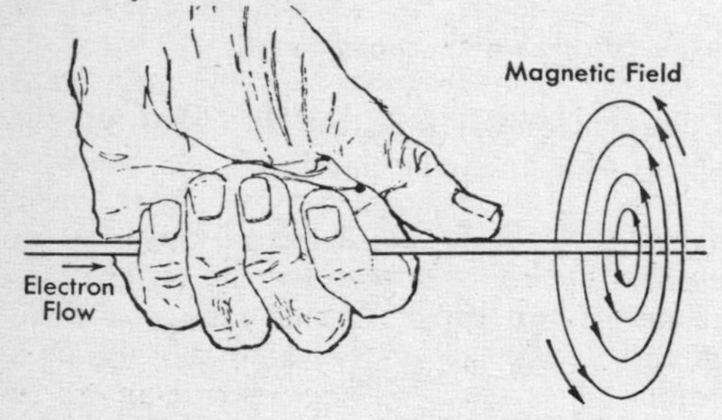

Grasp the conductor with the left hand so that the fingers point in the direction in which the north end of the compass needle is deflected, the thumb then points in the direction of electron flow along the conductor.

Note: Electrons always flow from negative to positive.

The electromagnet

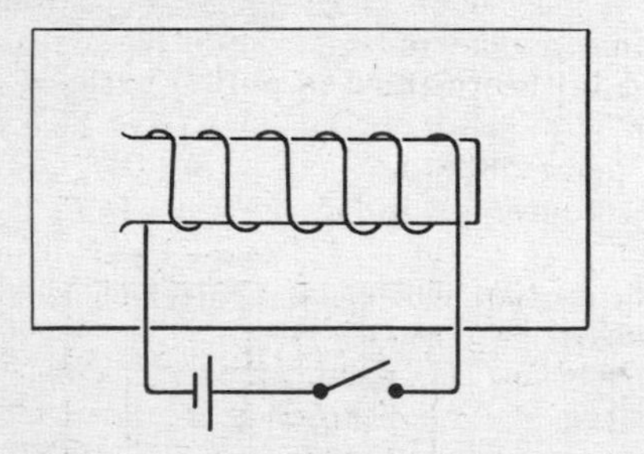

When a current is put through a single coil or several coils (helix) of wire, a magnetic field similar to that of a bar magnet is set up around the coil. The magnetic polarity of the field is easily determined with a compass.

The left hand helix rule

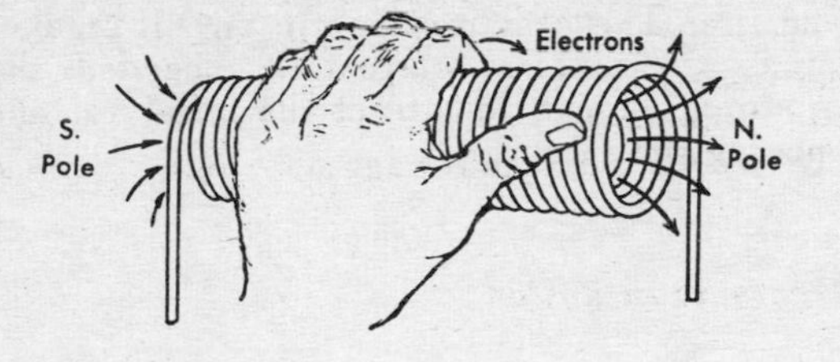

Grasp the coil with the left hand so that the fingers point in the direction of electron flow (from negative to positive), the thum b then points to the north pole of the magnetic field.

The *strength* of an electromagnet can be increased by

(a) adding a soft iron core

(b) increasing the current

(c) increasing the number of turns in the coil

Some Applications of Electromagnets

1. The electric bell

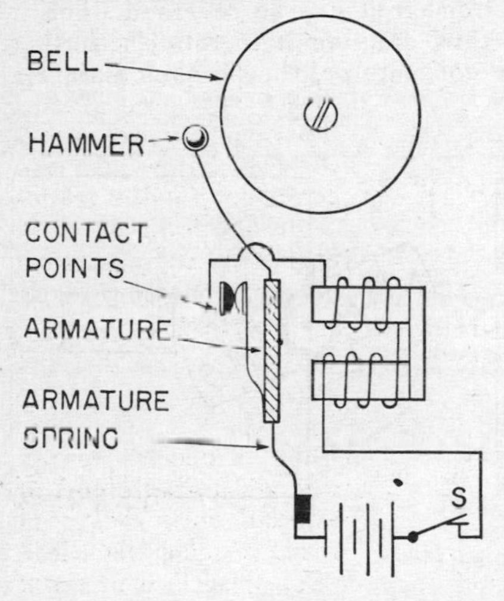

When at rest, the soft iron armature is held to the right by the spring, thus making contact with the contact screw. When the switch is closed electrons flow from the negative terminal through the coil, the contact screw and the armature to the positive terminal. The electromagnet is thus energized and attracts the armature. When the armature is attracted the contact points are open, electron flow stops, the magnetic field collapses and the armature is pulled to the right by the spring to start the cycle again.

2. The electric circuit breaker

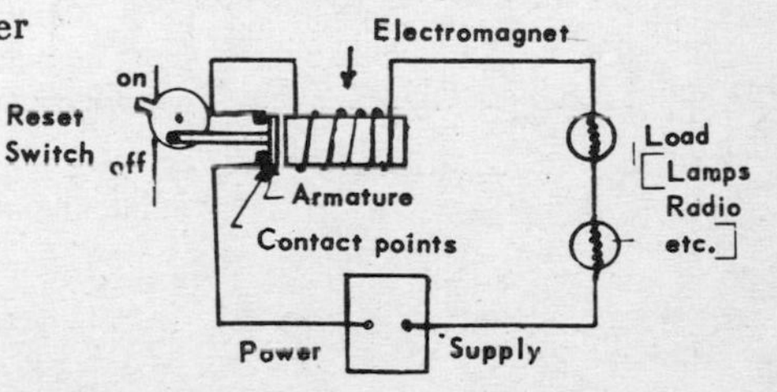

When a circuit is overloaded it draws excessive current that may result in overheating and fire. The electromagnetic circuit breaker is designed so that if the safe maximum current is exceeded, the magnetic field becomes strong enough to attract the armature, and stop electron flow by opening the circuit.

The Motor Principle

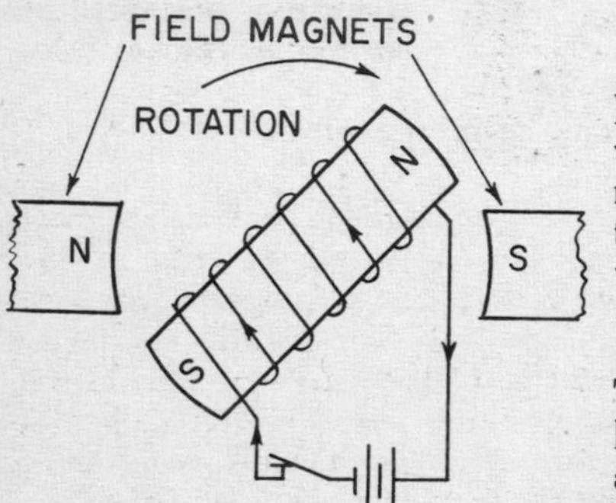

If a coil is suspended on a fine wire between two permanent magnets as shown, so that it is free to rotate approximately 180°, it will do so when the switch is closed.

The electromagnetic field created by the current flow in the coil reacts with the permanent magnetic field according to the laws of magnetism and results in partial rotation. By means of brushes and commutators, the current to the electromagnet can be reversed when it has rotated as far as it will go thus causing it to rotate a further 180°. Being free to slip over the commutator, the brushes maintain contact during rotation.

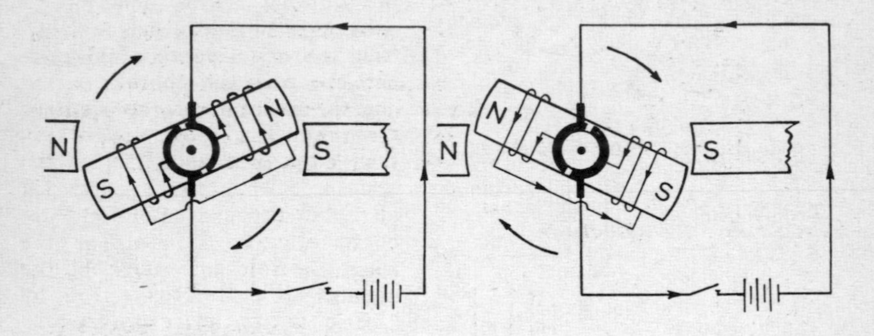

The Galvanometer

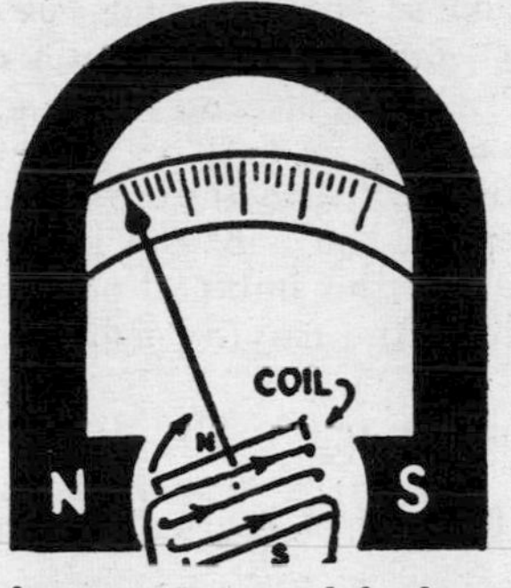

This is an instrument that operates on the motor principle and is used to detect the presence of a current in a circuit, determine its direction and relative strength.

An *Ammeter* is a galvanometer modified to measure current intensity in amperes. The modification is a *shunt* (bi-pass) resistor of very low resistance connected between the terminals. The ammeter must be connected in series in the circuit that is being tested and must not interfere with the circuit by drawing too much current. The shunt allows all of the current to flow "on by" except a very small proportion (usually not more than 0.05 amps) which passes through the moving coil. Thus the fine wire in the coil is protected against excessive current and overheating.

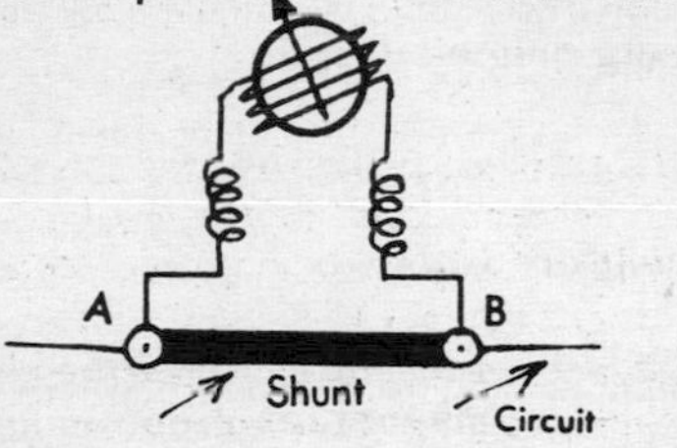

The *Voltmeter* measures PD between two points in a circuit and therefore must be connected in parallel. To keep the current through the voltmeter to a small fraction of that in the circuit being tested, there is a high resistance R, placed in series with the moving coil.

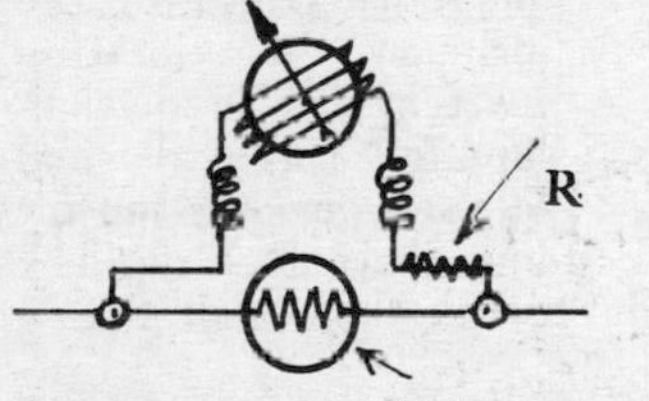

Electromagnetic Induction

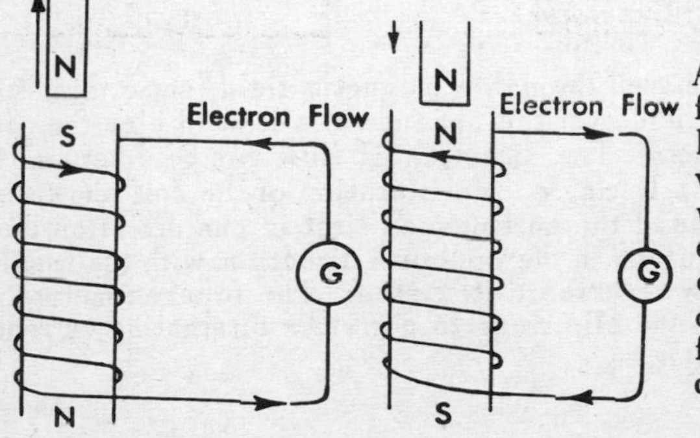

A changing magnetic field (such as created by moving magnet) in vicinity of a conductor will induce a flow of electrons in the conductor. The direction of the induced current flow changes with a change in direction or

Lenz's Law: The direction of the induced current is such that the magnetic field it creates opposes the motion of the magnetic field causing it.

Thus the magnet moving down into the coil induces a magnetic polarity which opposes (repels) the N of the lowering magnet. On leaving the lower end of the coil the induced polarity attracts (to oppose the motion of) the S pole of the moving magnet.

The *strength* of an induced magnetic field can be increased by

(a) Increasing the speed (rate of change) of the moving magnetic field

(b) Increasing the number of turns in the coil

(c) Increasing the strength of the changing magnetic field.

The Induction Coil – Primary and Secondary Coils

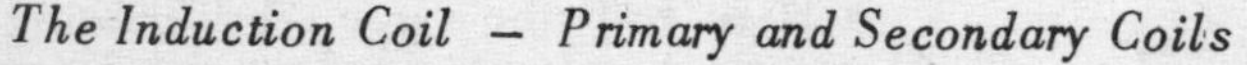

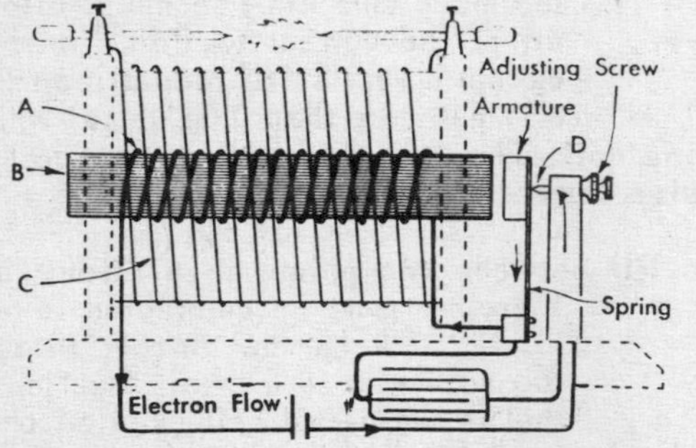

Instead of a moving bar magnet, an electromagnet (the primary circuit) is used. To create a rapid build up and collapse (change) in the magnetic field of the primary, a vibrating switch is used that opens (breaks) and closes (makes) the circuit just as is done in the electric bell. Thus there is a rapidly changing magnetic field over the secondary with the result that a high PD is induced in it.

The Alternating Current Generator

When a conductor is moved through a magnetic field (same thing as moving the magnetic field over the conductor) a flow of electrons is induced in the conductor. The direction of flow can be determined by Lenz's Law (try it). During one full rotation of the coil shown in the drawing, each side of the coil passes first in one direction through the lines of force then in the opposite direction, with the result that the electron flow reverses (alternates). The brushes maintain constant contact with the slip rings to carry the alternating current away from the generator.

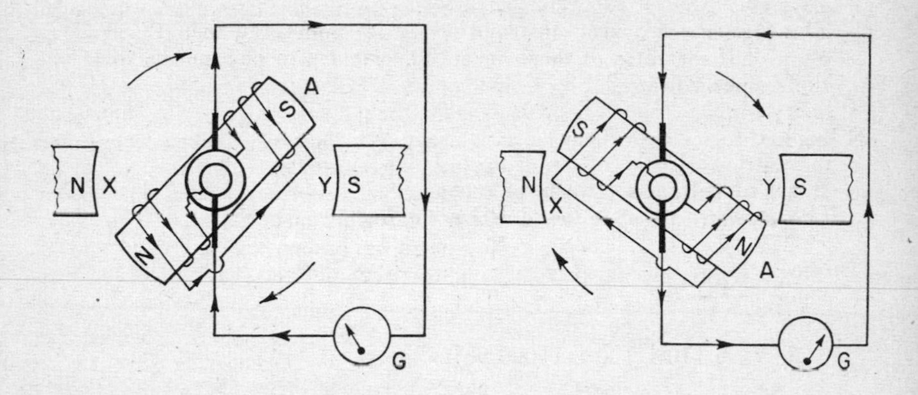

The DC Generator

The AC generator can be converted to DC by replacing the slip rings with commutator segments and brushes arranged as already studied in the DC motor. The DC motor can be used as a DC generator. If its armature is rotated mechanically, the coils will be moving in a magnetic field and acquire an induced current that will alternate once during each revolution. The brushes can be positioned so that at the instant the induced current reverses, each brush contacts the other half of the commutator. In this way the current enters each brush always in the same direction and we now have a DC generator.

Transformers

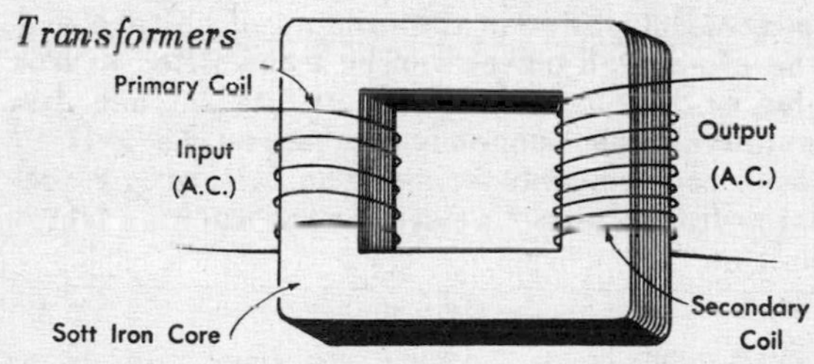

These are based on the principle of electromagnetic induction and operate on AC power. The primary is connected to the A C source which creates a rapidly reversing magnetic field (60 times per second) that builds up and collapses over the secondary inducing an EMF in it. A step-up transformer increases voltage, a step-down decreases voltage. The ratio of the voltage (input to output) is equal to the ratio of the number of turns, primary to secondary. That is, if the secondary has twice the number of turns then its PD will be twice that of the primary.

Example Problems

1. The primary of a step-up transformer is connected to a 110 V AC supply. If the ratio of turns is 1:100, primary to secondary, what is the output voltage?

Solution:

Ratio of voltages = Ratio of turns

$$\frac{V_s}{V_p} = \frac{N_s}{N_p}$$

V_s = PD secondary
N_s = No. turns secondary

$$\frac{V_s}{110} = \frac{100}{1}$$

$$\therefore V_s = 110 \times 100 = 11000 \text{ volts}$$

2. A transformer is required to step down a 120 V A.C. supply to 6 volts for a model electric train. If the primary coil has 1000 turns, how many must there be in the secondary?

Solution:

$$\frac{6}{120} = \frac{N_s}{1000} \quad \therefore N_s = \frac{6}{120} \times 1000 = 50 \text{ turns}$$

Power Distribution

Large current in a conductor means high temperature which in turn means heat (energy) losses. But power is the product of voltage and current, i.e. P = VI, therefore high power can be transmitted at low current if the PD is large. The use of AC electricity in long distance power transmission allows economical changes in PD by means of transformers as requirements arise. The following represents power transmission from a water power source such as Niagara, to distant communities.

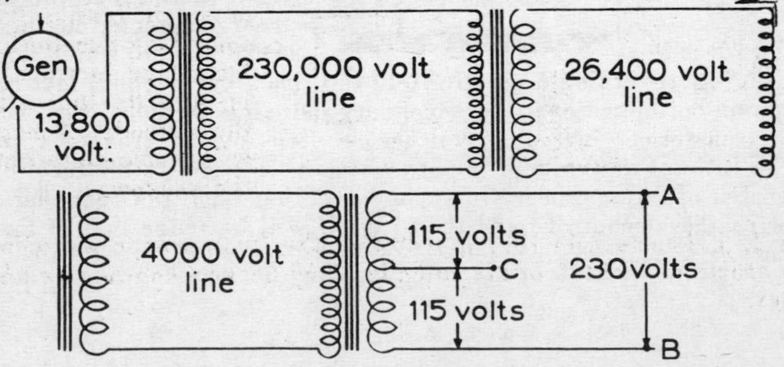

Unit 5 TOPICS IN MODERN PHYSICS

Electronics

Conduction in Gases – Cathode Rays

The sparks between the terminals of an induction coil, neon lights and lightening streaks are examples of conduction of electricity in gases. If a flame is brought near the knob of a charged electroscope the leaves will collapse whether the charge is positive or negative. The flame ionizes the air by setting some electrons free, positive ions or negative electrons are attracted to the knob, depending on its charge, until it is neutralized.

Gas conductivity improves as the pressure of the gas decreases. In the apparatus at left, at atmospheric pressure nothing is apparent in the tube, the spark continues between the terminals of the induction coil. As air is removed from the tube, a luminous streak appears between the cathode and anode. Definite luminous patterns appear at reduced pressures. A magnet will distort the luminous patterns. At about 10^{-6} atmospheres (one millionth of atmospheric pressure) the only glow visible is in the glass around the anode – a green fluorescence.

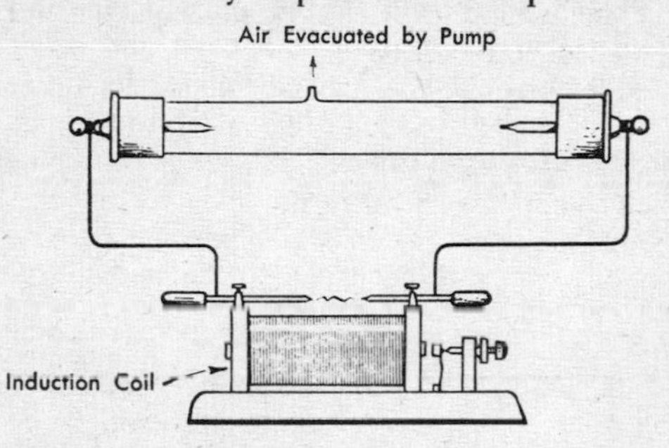

In Crooke's tube, a permanently evacuated tube, a shadow is cast by the cross indicating that something causing luminescence is travelling in straight lines from the cathode. A magnet will cause distortion of the shadow.

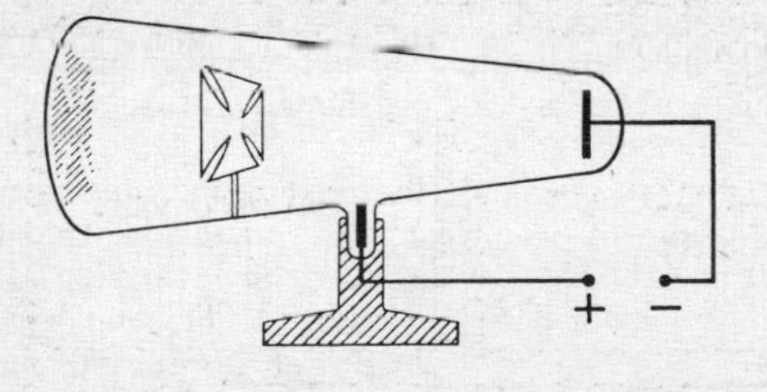

Sir J. J. Thomson in 1897 proved that the fluorescence was caused by electrons emitted by the cathode. They became known as *cathode rays*.

X-Rays

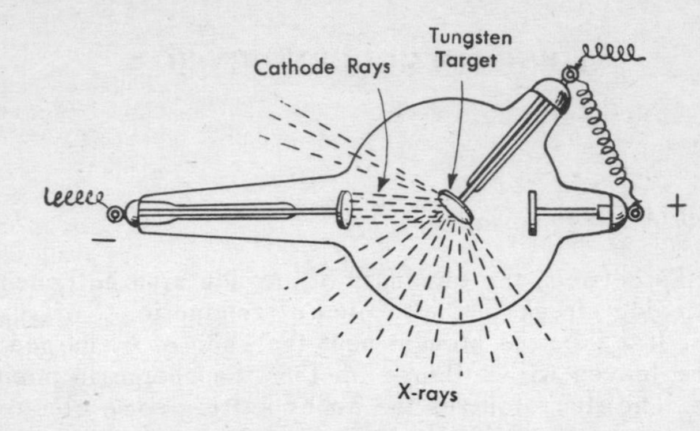

X-rays will originate at any surface where high speed electrons (cathode rays) are suddenly stopped. Certain metals form better targets (give off x-rays more readily) than others, eg. cesium and tungsten. X-rays form part of the spectrum in the portion beyond the ultra-violet. Many materials are transparent to x-rays and some materials emit light when exposed to them. X-rays cannot be deflected by strong electric or magnetic fields, yet they will ionize gases, eg., they will discharge an electroscope.

Photoelectricity

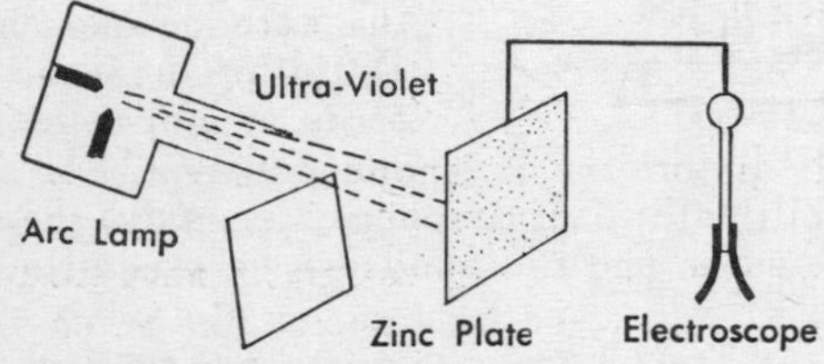

The zinc plate should be sand-papered to remove impurities then attached to an electroscope and charged negatively. Light from a carbon arc lamp will cause the electroscope and hence the plate to lose the charge: the energy from the ultra-violet rays is suffieient to knock electrons from the metal. The process is called photoelectric-emission. Cesium oxide, potassium and sodium will each emit electrons with ordinary light.

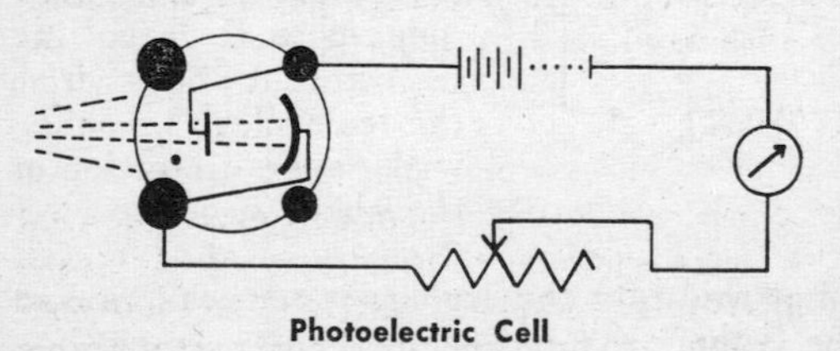

Photoelectric tubes operate on the principle that the greater the intensity of the incident light, the greater is the photoelectric emission. Thus the tubes can use light to control current intensity in a circuit.

Thermionic Emission

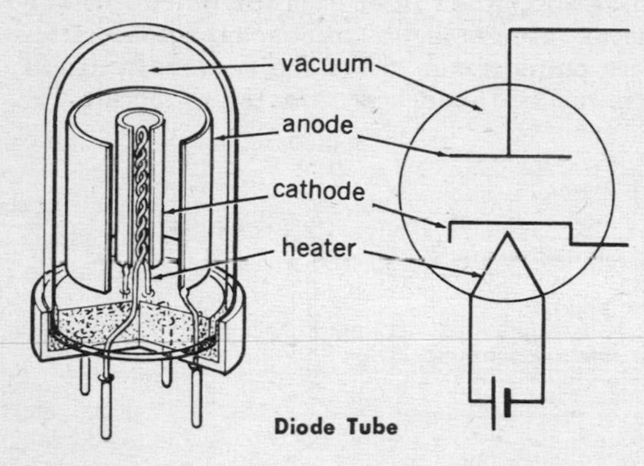

Diode Tube

At high enough temperatures large numbers of electrons will be emitted ("boil off") by some materials. The *diode* (two electrodes) vacuum tube uses this principle. When heated the cathode will emit electrons which will be attracted by the anode with the result that a current will flow in the circuit.

Rectification is the process of converting alternating current (AC) to direct current (DC) for use in radios, TV's etc. The diode can be used for this purpose since it will conduct electricity in one direction only. An AC entering the diode circuit is converted to a pulsating DC.

The Triode Tube and Amplification

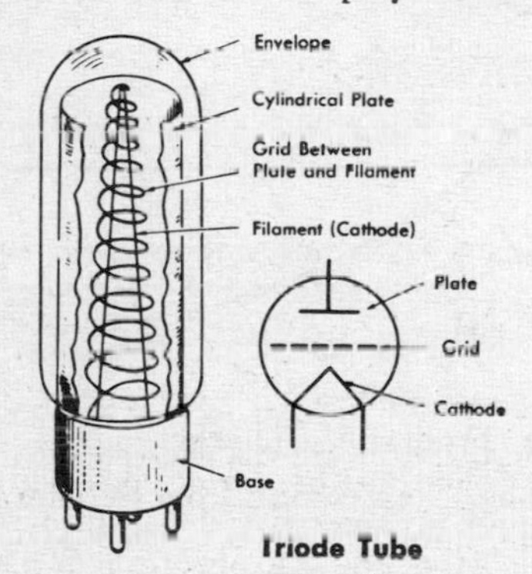

Triode Tube

The triode (tri = three) is a vacuum tube containing a third electrode in the form of a loose wire mesh or coil called the *grid*. When the grid is neutral, electrons flow past it without hindrance to the anode. But when it is made even weakly negative it will reduce (by repulsion) the flow of electrons from the cathode. When positive it will add to (amplify) the normal circuit flow. Thus very weak alternating voltages such as those from a receiver antenna, if attached to a grid will be amplified by the triode.

The TV Camera and Picture Tube

The cathode and anode are combined in the camera to make up what is called an "electron gun" to produce a fine beam of electrons (cathode rays) which, by appropriately charged vertical and horizontal deflectors, is made to "scan" the image with horizontal lines from top to bottom just as a persons eyes do in reading a page. The signal plate on the inside face of the tube is thin enough to be transparent to light and is kept positive relative to the photo sensitive material behind it (see diagram). When light from the object strikes the photo sensitive material, electrons are released (photoelectrically) in numbers which are proportional to the light intensity (light areas more, dark areas fewer). These are attracted to the signal

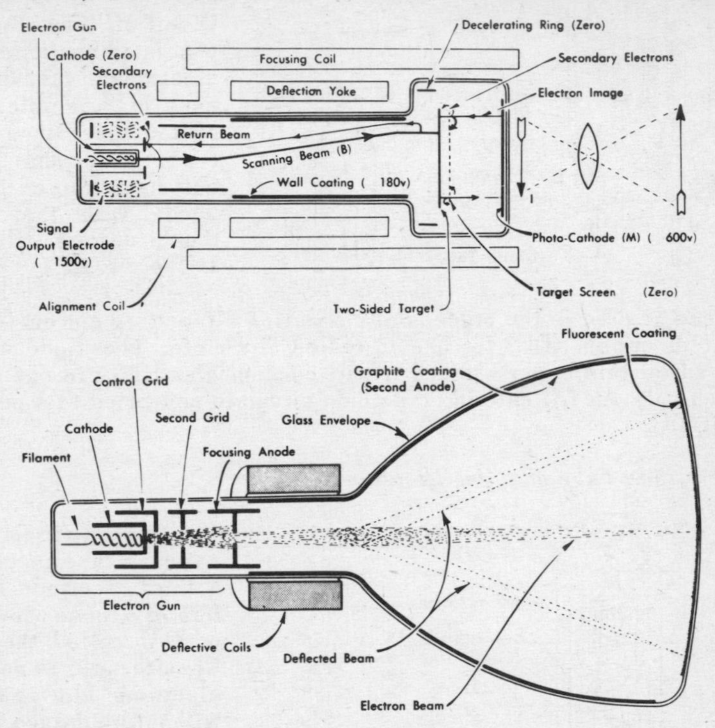

plate (+) and are replaced in the photo sensitive material by the cathode rays. The signal plate then, receives a charge whose intensity varies with the light intensity (shading) of the object. This current is amplified through triodes and is transmitted as radio waves. The T. V. receiver (picture) tube also has an electron gun which scans the fluorescent face of the tube in exact synchronization with the camera gun. The intensity of the electron beam and therefore the fluorescence on the screen of the picture tube, is varied by the video signal from the camera. Thus a picture of the object is duplicated on the screen. The electron beam covers the complete picture tube by scanning, in about 1/30 of a second so that its motion is imperceptable to us and the time between complete scannings (separate complete pictures) is a little less than the time between frames of a movie projector.

Atomic Structure

By measuring the amount of deflection of a cathode ray (electron beam) in known magnetic and electric field strengths, Sir J.J. Thomson in 1897 was able to calculate the ratio of the electric charge "e" to the mass "m", i.e. e/m, of the electron. He found the value to be $e/m = 1.76 \times 10^{11}$ coulombs per kilogram and that it was constant for all elements used in the cathode. At the same time he found the velocity of electrons to be about one tenth that of light.

R.A. Millikan in 1906 in his famous oil drop experiment determined the charge on an electron to be $e = 1.6 \times 10^{-19}$ coulombs. A droplet of oil from an atomizer spray was allowed to enter the region between two oppositely charged, flat plates through a pin-hole. By means of x-rays he was able to charge the droplet at will. By comparing the rate at which the droplet fell a known distance in a neutral state to the rate it moved the same distance with a known charge on it he was able to determine e.

With this value and Thomson's e/m value Millikan readily determined the mass of the electron:

$$\frac{e}{m} = 1.76 \times 10^{11} = \frac{1.6 \times 10^{-19}}{m}$$

$$\therefore m = \frac{1.6 \times 10^{-19}}{1.76 \times 10^{11}} = 9.1 \times 10^{-31} \text{ kg}$$

Radioactivity

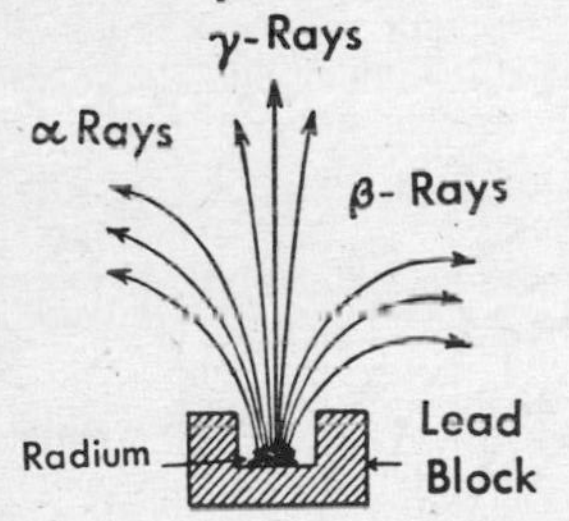

Near the end of the 19th century Rutherford was able to show that radium emitted beta (β) rays which were attracted to a positive plate and d (alpha) rays that were attracted to a negative plate. Gamma (γ) rays discovered later, undergo no deflection.

The d rays are now known to be nuclei of helium atoms (2 neutrons 2 protons), which are weak radiations that can be stopped in a short distance by air. Beta rays are made up of electrons travelling at nearly the speed of light (high energy) but can be stopped by thin metal sheet. Gamma rays are high energy x-rays which travel at the speed of light and are able to penetrate several inches of lead.

Radioactive materials spontaneously disintegrate by emitting α or β particles, and energy in the form of   rays, until they degenerate into new materials that are no longer radioactive, eg., radium becomes lead.

The rate of radioactive decay is constant for a particular substance and cannot be changed by temperature or pressure changes. A piece of radium will decay so that 1 kgm for example, would become ½ kgm in 1620 years and this would become ¼ kgm in another 1620 years and so on. Thus the "half-life" of radium is 1620 years.

Radiation ionizes gases thus its presence can be detected by an instrument such as the Geiger Counter. This consists of an aluminum tube, the cathode, and a central electrode (anode) insulated from the cathode. Radiation will pass through the tube, ionize the gas inside, cause a current to flow and deflect the galvanometer. The intensity of the current is a measure of the radiation intensity.

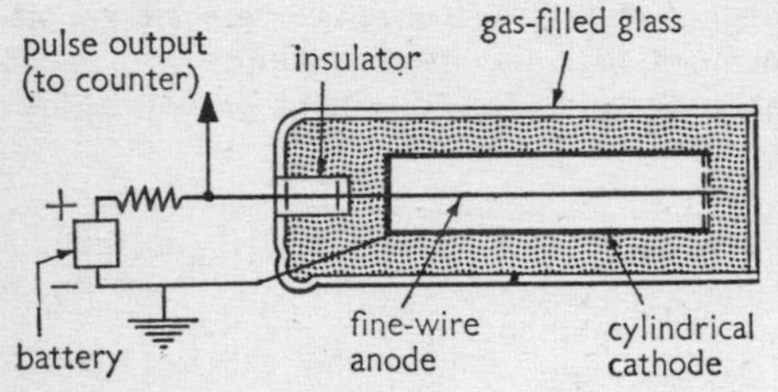

The Atomic Nucleus

Rutherford (at McGill 1910) used d particles from radioactive nuclei to bombard gold foil 160 atoms deep (9 x 10^{-6} cm thick). A rare no. of deflections of the d particles, which were caused by particles of comparable weight, confirmed his model of the "nuclear atom" i.e. a nucleus of heavy particles of positive charge orbitted by light negative charges (electrons).

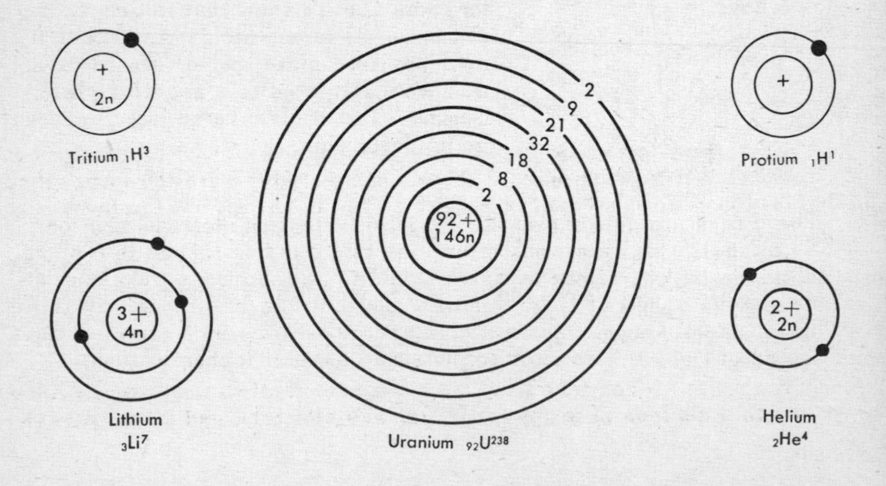

The typical nucleus has a radius of about 5×10^{-13} cm which is small compared to the diameter of the atom (10^{-8} cm) and this accounts for the "rare" no. of deflections in Rutherfords experiment, i.e. an atom is mostly empty space.

The density of the nucleus is very high, it constitutes over 99% of the atom's weight and is about 100 trillion times the density of water.

In 1913 Niels Bohr proposed his theory of the simplest atom, that of hydrogen: The nucleus, a positive particle is orbitted by an electron of equal but opposite charge and the centrifugal force of the circling electron is exactly balanced by the electro static attraction between the two charges – so far in agreement with Rutherford – but he added that each electron moves in an orbit of definite radius according to rigid mathematical laws. He decided that electrons at greater radii possess more energy than those nearer the nucleus and that when jumping from an outer to an inner orbit there is a corresponding release of energy (light) called a quantum or photon. Thus light is produced in squirts or bundles of rays called quanta or photons. Furthermore, photons are absorbed when electrons move to outer orbits (i.e. higher energy levels).

The *atomic number* of an atom is the number of protons (charges) in its nucleus and is peculiar to each element. It is the lower left subscript when written with the symbol eg. $_2He$; $_8O$; $_{92}U$. In a neutral atom the number of protons equals the number of electrons.

In 1932 a second nuclear particle, one without a charge named the neutron, was discovered by J. Chadwick.

The *mass number* of an atom represents the total number of protons and neutrons and is written on the right above the symbol.

eg. Helium $_2He^4$ Oxygen $_8O^{16}$ Uranium $_{92}U^{238}$

Uranium has 146 neutrons and 92 protons in its nucleus.

Rutherford later discovered that some atoms of the same element differed from each other in mass but otherwise were the same, they retained the same number of protons and electrons but the number of neutrons (about the same wt. as a proton) was different. Such atoms are called *isotopes*. eg. $_{92}U^{235}$ is an isotope of uranium, $_1H^2$ (deuterium) is an isotope of hydrogen and many others exist.

Nuclear Physics – Nuclear Reaction

Rutherford found that when an α particle (helium nucleus) collided with a nucleus of nitrogen ($_7N^{14}$) it was absorbed and in the process a neutron was released. This left a new nucleus with one proton and 2 neutrons more than the original nitrogen nucleus – an isotope of oxygen, $_8O^{17}$.

Many ways of artificially producing high speed neutrons and protons (atomic bullets) have been developed for the purpose of scattering, analysing and synthesizing nuclei and in the process, a means of releasing previously undreamed of quantities of energy was discovered.

Nuclear Fission

Of the forces that bind the nucleus, (neutrons and protons) together little is known except that they are far greater than the forces involved in gravity, electrostatics and magnetism. They are about a million times greater than attractive forces between molecules and about 10^{38} times greater than gravity!

Atomic fission is akin to a TNT explosion where a mechanical shock produced by the explosion of an unstable molecule triggers other unstable molecules into a chain reaction. No heat was necessary to start it.

In all cases of fission (division) of nuclei the collective mass of the separated particles is less than the original mass of the nucleus.

This "mass defect" has been converted to energy in the form of light and heat according to Einstiens famous $E = mc^2$, where E is the energy released, m is the "mass defect" and c is the velocity of light. It is also a measure of the binding force of the nucleus.

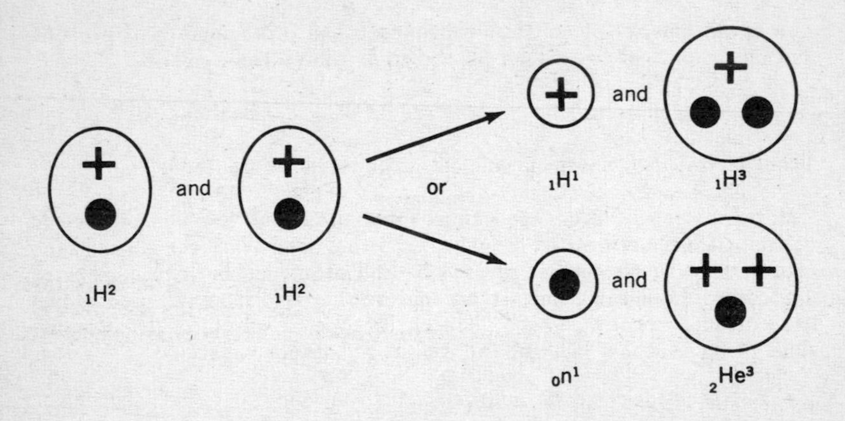

The unstable (radio active) isotope of uranium $_{92}U^{235}$, spontaneously fissions to form two nucleii which separate at great speed, and between one and four neutrons. If the number of unstable atoms is plentiful then neutrons set free by their spontaneous fission will trigger more unstable atoms until a chain reaction is set up. In ordinary uranium there are about 22 unstable atoms per gram – not enough to create fission on a large scale. The size of the piece of uranium and the proportion of $_{92}U^{235}$ atoms present are critical factors in the production of the fission bomb. They can be controlled by varying the purity and the size of the uranium used.

Nuclear Fusion

This has its comparison in chemical combustion where molecules *combine* (eg. Hydrogen snd Oxygen fuse to form water) and their reaction releases energy (heat, light). To fuse, the molecules must collide violently thus heat (to the ignition temp.) is necessary to trigger the reaction and there must be enough fuel to continue the process.

In the 1920's and 1930's, physicists using atomic bullets found that if protons were accelerated to high enough energies they could break through the repulsive force (+) of the target nucleus and fuse therewith. The final mass was again, less than the collective mass of the initial particles. The difference in masses was released as energy according to $E = mc^2$. The nuclear fusion fuel is deuterium, an isotope of hydrogen $_1H^2$, found in "heavy" water.

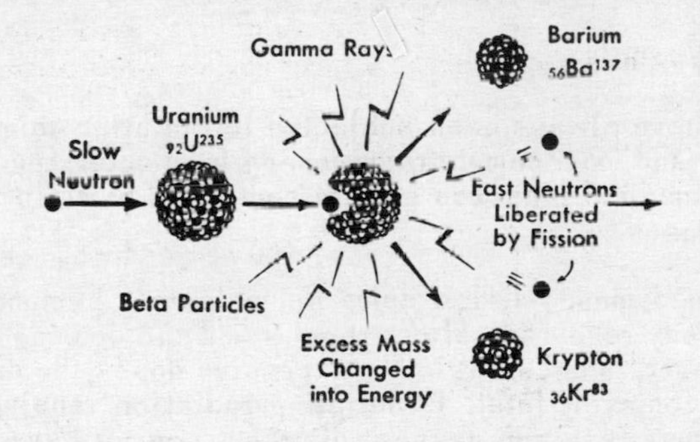

One difference between nuclear fusion and chemical fusion is in the ignition temperature. Something like 350 million degrees are necessary to cause fusion of the deuterium nuclei. The trigger is therefore a fission bomb.

The Atomic Age

Even in the small quantities in which deuterium exists in natural water, there is in one gallon, the energy equivalent of over 300 gallons of gasoline. Its cost of extraction would make its overall costs as a fuel less than 1% of that of coal.

In Canada and the U.S.A. power requirements are doubling about every 10 years. Comparing the advantages of the fuels: The quantity of uranium available in the earth is about 100 times the quantity of other fuels (which are dwindling); the supply of deuterium will dry up only when the earth's water dries up. The radiation hazards of fusion reactions are far less serious than those of the fission reaction and finally, the former yields a great deal more energy.

The more important uses of the energy available from nuclear reactions are probably in steam generating for turbines which have applications in transportation and the generation of electric power. The bi-products (isotopes) are also useful in research and industry. Earth moving projects are near the top of the list: a 100 kiloton H-bomb (energy equivalent to 100,000 tons of TNT) will move 12 million tons of earth in about 30 seconds.

Some Applications of Radioactive Materials

The cobalt bomb produces radiation that is used to help destroy cancer cells. Radioactive atoms are used as tracers in solutions swallowed by humans or absorbed by plants; Geiger counters will trace the paths of the atoms and help to analyse body and plant processes. A cobalt bomb is also useful in "x-raying" metals in search for defects. Isotopes (radioactive) are used in controlling the thickness, to extremely accurate values, of sheet metal in rolling mills.

Radiation Hazards

Humans have always been subjected to radiation from materials in the earth and from cosmic rays coming from outer space. X-rays are used for medical purposes but are controlled by trained technicians to safe doses.

Radiation damages living cells but unless it becomes excessive, natural body resources effect repairs and the damage goes unnoticed. However, in uncontrolled or excessive doses the damage can be crippling or even fatal. Penetrating radiation received externally (γ rays) may result in nausea, diarrhea, haemorrhage and if severe enough, death. Localized concentrations of external radiation may cause burns and loss of hair; entry through the mouth or lessions in the skin may cause anaemia and cancer.

For the purpose of radiation measurement a unit of intensity called the *roentgen*, (r), is used. Briefly, the roentgen involves the amount of ionization created in a cubic centimeter of air by γ or x-rays, (the Geiger counter measures this).

Distance, time and shielding are important factors in radiation effects. Intensity falls off rapidly with distance from the source; its effects are proportional (multiplied by) the duration of exposure; almost anything in its path reduces its intensity. During a 24 hour period fatalities may occur, depending on individual resistance, at between 200 and 500 r; at about 100 r, nausea; around 50 r, temporary blood defects; up to 25 r no noticeable effects are evident. Radiation intensity can be reduced by about 90% by a shield of either 2½ inches of lead, 4 inches of iron, 1 foot of concrete or 2 feet of earth.

NOTES